These

500

Fascinating Facts

Are Quotable

This book is full of "filler Material", as well as interesting articles, for newspapers, magazines, periodicals, radio and television.

All 500 facts are numbered individually. They can be used daily, weekly, or monthly, in groups or individually.
Design your own headings.

All we ask is that credit be given the Harold Warp Pioneer Village (non-profit) Foundation, Minden, Nebraska*.

Published
By

HAROLD WARP
PIONEER VILLAGE
FOUNDATION ®

*Except where gleaned
from another source

Minden, Nebraska 68959

i

Published
By

Minden, Nebraska 68959

Harold Warp was born December 21, 1903 on a farm near Minden, Nebraska and died April 8, 1994 at the age of 90 years. He is survived by his son, Harold G. Warp, who succeeds him as President of the Harold Warp Pioneer Village Foundation.

This Is Not A Book of Fiction

500
Fascinating Facts

(Each Numbered In Lower Right Corner)

MOST OF WHICH CAN BE
VARIFIED IF PROPERLY RESEARCHED

— EXAMPLES —

B.F. Goodrich made Mr. Winton pay the cost of making the first set of pneumatic tires for an automobile in 1896, because Goodrich doubted there would ever be enough demand for such tires to pay for the dies themselves.

(Fascinating Fact #433)

France forfeited $5,000 they had paid down in the purchase of the Wright Brothers' basic flying machine patents for $200,000 in 1906, (when the U.S. Government was not interested), because France was led to believe the Wright Brothers were "fakers".

(Fascinating Fact #122)

One day in April, 1900, Harry Stevens, who ran the frankfurter stall at the New York Polo Grounds, shouted "They're hot, red hot, get your dachshund sausages while they're hot." A newspaper cartoonist, Tad Dorgan, hearing Stevens' sales pitch, drew a cartoon of two frankfurters barking at each other and titled it "Hot Dogs". They have been hot dogs ever since.

(Fascinating Facts #319)

HAROLD WARP FOUNDATION
PIONEER VILLAGE ®
Minden, Nebraska 68959

iii

500 Fascinating Facts

500 Fascinating Facts

500 Fascinating Facts

500 Fascinating Facts

500 Fascinating Facts

500 Fascinating Facts

500 Fascinating Facts

500 Fascinating Facts

500 Fascinating Facts

When a light was shone into a leaky bucket, the light followed the water through the hole and lit up the floor. John Tyndall discovered this in 1870 and today millions of telephone conversations are carried across the Atlantic and Pacific oceans on clear glass fibres, smaller than a needle's eye, buried beneath the sea, using Tyndall's discovery that light will follow a clear tube, whether it be a stream of water, plastic rod, or clear glass fibres.   1

John Tyndall's leaky bucket sparked worldwide conversations.

Gene McDonald conceived the idea of making Zenith radios to contact people halfway around the world while he was on a trip to the North Pole with McMillan in 1920. He used a radio he took with him, made by two Chicago boys, Karl Hassel and Ralph Mathews, with call letters ZN9. When McDonald returned to Chicago he contacted those two boys and launched "Zenith" radio company with a million dollars he had made from the sale of an auto finance company, while in his 20s.   2

Gene McDonald's North Pole expedition sparked Zenith Radio Corp.

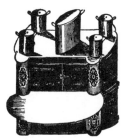

For many centuries folks believed that if they enclosed a flame it would explode. It was Ben Franklin who invented the stove in 1740, that slipped right in front of the customary fireplace. It was 100 years later, however, (1850s) before folks really started using stoves instead of fireplaces.   3

Folks were afraid that Franklin's stove would explode.

You may think rocking chairs are "old as the hills", but believe it or not, the first rocking chair was made in 1763 by none other than Benjamin Franklin for his own use. He also had a fan above the back of the rocker, so he could fan himself as he rocked.   4

Folks went for Franklin's rocking chair but not his fan.

Folks had lived for thousands of years with ox-carts, grease lamps and open hearths. Then in the fleeting glimpse of a single century of eternal time,

Our age of discoveries - a mere fleeting glimpse of eternal time.

man progressed from grease lamps to television and from ox-carts to interplanetary travel. This astounding progress in one century is shown in actuality at Nebraska's #1 attraction, the Harold Warp Pioneer Village at Minden in south central Nebraska, where over 50,000 items are on display that were invented or discovered by our forefathers and by ourselves, since 1830 when our industrial revolution began. 5

It was after 1830 that man learned how to roll steel into sheets to hold steam under pressure so as to produce mechanical horsepower (Peter Cooper's "Tom Thumb" locomotive 8-28-1830) and to make scouring steel plows that turn the soil (Wm. Woods in Pittsburg, PA made cast steel for John Deere, Moline, Illinois 1846). It was after 1800 that man learned how to draw wire into continuous lengths, to carry bridges (Ichabod Washburn, Worcester Mass. – continuous wire 1850 – became American Steel & Wire Co.) as well as for carrying electricity. On these simple achievements is based our astounding progress in the 20th century. 6

Our progress commenced when steel could be rolled into sheets (in 1830) and when wire could be drawn continuously (in 1850).

The oxen were a blessing to the early settlers as they pressed 'Westward". Once considered useless – the offspring of a milk cow – they could carry burdens and pull wagons over terrain that horses could not. Also, the ox was not as attractive to the marauding Indians who wanted fast mounts. This passive animal was used for plowing until the time that it was needed for food. 7

Indians would not steal oxen and they could be used for food when too old to work.

Children trained oxen calves.

During pioneer days children earned their own keep. For example, youngsters were responsible for training oxen calves to carry fuel for fires and water for washing. At the Harold Warp Pioneer Village in south central Nebraska, you can see the evolution of transportation from ox carts to jet planes, even children's ox-carts and ox-yokes for calves. 8

The rugged Conestoga wagon got its name from where it was first built in the 1830s on the banks of Conestoga Creek in Lancaster County, Pennsylvania. Its floor curved downward to the middle, approximately six inches lower than the ends of the body, so the load would not shift while crossing rugged terrain. It was also made so logs could be put under the axles to ford streams.   9

More than a million Conestoga wagons crossed the Alleghenies in the 1800s.

When the Walker and Frink stage coaches commenced passenger service between Detroit and Chicago in 1836, they had to ford rivers, as there were no bridges. When they came to the Calumet River at the south end of Lake Michigan, the shallowest waters were in front of the entrance of the river, known as the delta. Some passengers would get hysterical when the stage driver would seemingly head for the middle of Lake Michigan while fording the shallow waters of the Calumet River delta.   10

Walker & Frink Stages seemed to head into Lake Michigan while crossing Calumet River Delta.

By 1860, when speedier travel became available by train, Walker and Frink had gained control of all stage lines in and out of Chicago, covering a radius of 1000 miles. Their headquarters were at Lake and Clark streets. In those days, Indian country commenced at Fullersberg, where the Graue waterpowered mill was built on Salt Creek in 1838, replaced in 1947 in Chicago's western suburb of Hinsdale.   11

By 1860, Mr. Frink's Stages controlled traffic in and out of Chicago.

All stage coach travel in and out of Chicago was controlled by one man in 1860. His name was Frink, who started the Walker and Frink stage lines between Chicago and Detroit in 1836. He had bought up all Chicago competitors by 1860 when speedier railroad travel converged to take over. A Walker and Frink stage coach is on display at the Harold Warp Pioneer Village, Minden, Nebr.   12

When rails crossed the U.S. in 1869, the end was near for stage travel.

Henry Wells

W.G. Fargo

Wells-Fargo stages first reached Denver in 1859. They employed 5000 men, owned 40,000 oxen and mules, and had 313 stage robberies.

Wells-Fargo stage lines were formed by Henry Wells and W.G. Fargo in 1852. They used Abbott-Downing Coaches, pulled by four or six galloping steeds that supposedly could outrun the Indian ponies. (Indians originally had no horses and many white men lost their lives for their horses) The coaches cost about $1250 and the fare from St. Joseph, Missouri to Denver was $175. Baggage allowed was 25 pounds. The first stage reached Denver in 1859. To traverse the continent required about two months, with stations 75 miles to 125 miles apart.   13

HAROLD WARP
PIONEER VILLAGE
Minden, Neb. 68959 FOUNDATION

In 1865 Wells-Fargo were by far the most prominent stage lines in the West, but their dominance was short lived, because rails spanned the country in 1869. At their height, Wells-Fargo employed five thousand men, had four thousand wagons and over forty thousand oxen and mules (Indians would steal horses). Between 1870 and 1884, $415,312.00 was stolen from Wells-Fargo in three hundred thirteen stage robberies and four train robberies. A Wells-Fargo stagecoach and a steel money chest is on display at the Harold Warp Pioneer Village at Minden, Nebraska.   14

Wells-Fargo bought Concord Coaches by the train load. They cost $1400, carried 6 to 8 people, capacity 2 tons.

They had to be sturdy.

The Concord Coach (1835-1885) was made of the finest white ash, oak, elm, and prime basswood, by the Abbott-Downing Company of Concord, New Hampshire. This light, elegant, durable leather hung vehicle revolutionized Western travel. The wheels were heavy, with broad iron tires that would not sink in soft mud, and set wide apart – 5 ft. 2 in. – to keep the coach from tipping. The body, reinforced with iron, swung on leather straps 3½ in. wide, that allowed it to rock back and forth to make pulling it over rough ground easy on the horses, and at the same time serve as shock absorbers for the passengers. The full-bodied Concord coach weighed 3,000 pounds, had a capacity of two tons (4,000 pounds), could accommodate 6 to 9 passengers inside, with an unlimited number on top, and cost $1,400. It truly opened the West to travel.   15

Yellowstone Coaches pulled by six horses, took 5 days to tour the park and cost $40.

While horses rested, occupants imbibed.

A typical example of the world-renowned Concord coach, made in Concord, N.H. This was one of thirty made for the Wells Fargo Company for the Rockies-California service in the 70s and 80s.

Black Bart (Charles E. Bolton).

Gypsy wagons were burned when owner died.

307,000 visitors were hauled through Yellowstone Park between 1880 and 1916, by the one hundred sixty-five Yellowstone wagons pulled by four and six horse teams. The trip through the park took five days and cost $40.00, including meals and lodging. Six horse drivers were paid seventy-five dollars per month and four horse drivers fifty dollars. One of those Yellowstone wagons is on display at the Harold Warp Pioneer Village at Minden, Nebraska.   16

Private stage coaches even sported secret bars. One such coach on display at the Harold Warp Pioneer Village at Minden, Nebraska belonged to E.J. Lehman, who owned the Boston Store in Chicago, competitor to Marshall Field and Co. This coach was stored for over 75 years at Fox Lake, Illinois before it was brought to the Pioneer Village.   17

The word "Coach" comes from Kocs, a town in Hungary where an early coachlike vehicle was built in the 1450s.   18

A poet-at-heart was the most notorious stage coach robber, Charles E. Bolton, who committed 28 robberies, always leaving doggerel poetry at each holdup and signing his name "Black Bart". Wells Fargo iron money boxes, built into their stage coaches, that were used to transport millions of dollars in gold as insurance against highway robbers, can be seen at the Harold Warp Pioneer Village in south central Nebraska.   19

According to English gypsy custom, the van in which Mrs. Sarah Bunce spent 60 years travel from county fairs to races was burned.   20

The gypsy wagon now at Harold Warp's Pioneer Village was brought over from France in 1950 because none could be found in the U.S.A.   21

Leland Stanford

Bankers laughed at them, yet railroading got its necessary boost from four storekeepers who decided to build a railroad to link California with the East. They were Leland Stanford, Collis Huntington, Mark Hopkins and Charles Crocker. On May 10, 1869, their dream came true when the Central Pacific joined the Union Pacific in Utah. Vintage locomotives and other early railroad paraphernalia in the evolution of transportation can be seen at the Harold Warp Pioneer Village in south central Nebraska.   22

The first railroad spanned the United States in 1869. Thirty years later most of the railroads that spanned the West had gone into receivership and were taken over by two men, Jim Hill of St. Paul and Ed Harriman of New York.

Edward Harriman

Jet airliners commenced spanning the United States in 1960. Thirty years later most airlines had gone into receivership and were being taken over by very few men, duplicating what happened to the railroads just a century earlier.   23

Union Pacific was the first railroad to span the nation in 1869 and the first to go into receivership thirty years later. Pan American was the first airline to span the oceans and was the first to go into receivership just one hundred years after Union Pacific went broke.   24

James Jerome Hill

Early trains rode on steel straps spiked to wooden stringers. The spikes would work loose and bend over, which resulted in a bump as each car wheel went over it until the spike broke off. Thus many loose rails caused serious accidents.   25

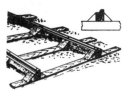

Early day rails wrecked trains.

#967 took its last trip to The Pioneer Village on rubber tires.

Baldwin Locomotive #967, built in 1889, that pulled trains across the country for the next fifty-five years on steel rails, took its last ride to the Harold Warp Pioneer Village at Minden, Nebraska on rubber tires. Reason: The highway department refused to let old #967 cross US Highway #6 unless it was on rubber tires, which it did in May, 1955.   26

Many railroads, including the Northern Pacific, started with tiny Porter narrow gauge locomotives with flared smokestacks.   27

Early locomotive smokestacks were flared to prevent forest and prairie fires.

Smokestacks on early locomotives were flared to catch sparks from the fire box, that could cause forest or prairie fires. The flared smokestacks were made like present day dust collectors, to catch burning embers.   28

On December 29, 1961 the last Grand Trunk train was pulled across the state of Michigan on regular service by a steam locomotive. This was 92 years after the first steam locomotives pulled a Union Pacific train across the United States on rails in 1869.   29

92 years elapsed between the first and last passenger train across Michigan.

Horse cars tended to tip on speedy turns.

Horse drawn streetcars made their appearance in 1832 in New York, and Omaha's first horse-car came in 1867. (Now at Pioneer Village) Hay was used on the floor to keep the passengers' feet warm. They had no stoves. Danger from overturning was a part of the trip because most horse-cars were top-heavy and tumbled easily when turning. At the Harold Warp Pioneer Village in south central Nebraska, you can see Omaha's first horse-car, San Francisco's O'Farrel Street cable-car, Ft. Collins, Colorado early electric trolley car, as well as omnibuses depot hacks and locomotives.   30

Even in street car travel people resented change.

Pranks of grandad's day.

People resent change so the first bike resembled a horse in 1816.

Albert Pope offered the first high wheeler in 1878.

Starley introduced the safety bike in 1887.

Prior to 1906 a Chicago ordinance banned electric trolley wires in the Chicago Loop. Horses had to be hitched to electric cars entering the downtown area. Horse-car service operated on Chicago's Madison Street route from May 1859 to August 1906. That month, horses used in cable car service were replaced by electric street cars. Chicago then had 94 miles of cable cars. 31

In "horse and buggy" and "cable car" days, and before the advent of electric street lights, mischievous boys would cut out cardboard ghosts and attach them to the moving underground cable of deserted streets, in the dark of night. This could certainly scare the "wits" out of any homeward bound late imbiber. 32

Bicycles – Although the first bicycle was merely a toy horse on wheels in 1816, most improvements can be credited to Americans over the next 150 years. The bicycle evolved slowly. The first two-wheel bicycle was invented by Baron Von Drais in Germany in 1816. He merely copied a horse with wheels between the front and back legs. It was propelled by striking ones' feet against the ground and became known as a "Hobby Horse". It was later patented in the U.S. in 1819 by W.K. Clarkson of New York. 33

Albert Pope of Philadelphia made the first practical "High-Wheeler" bicycle in 1878. It had solid rubber tires, wooden rims, wire spokes and sold for $313. The front wheel traveled 15 feet with one step of each foot, providing the rider didn't take a "header" from his high perch. Over three million high-wheelers were sold in the "Gay 90s". 34

The modern "Safety Bike" was introduced in 1887 by Starley with both wheels the same size, with pedals between them with chain drive to the rear wheel. 35

Dunlop's pneumatic tires in 1890 and Townsends coaster brake that same year made bicycles practical.

The first pneumatic tire was put on a bicycle by Dunlap in 1890, but the "Safety Bike" didn't really start outselling "High Wheelers" until Townsend of Bristol, Connecticut invented the Coaster brake that went on the rear wheel hub, still made the same 100 years later. 36

A new fad evolved in kids' bikes.

The bicycle has not changed since 1887, when Starley introduced his "safety" bike. The safety of "Low Rover", using the same 15 to 1 gear ratio with smaller wheels and a larger sprocket, was scorned by the high-wheeled "He-Men" for many years. 37

On June 30, 1899, Charley Murphy did the incredible. He rode his bike behind a speeding locomotive, managing to cover a measured mile in the fantastic time of 57 4/5 seconds. "Mile-a-minute" Murphy's record was not broken for 42 years. 38

Fred Marriot's Stanley Steamer reached 197 miles per hour before flying apart in 1906.

In 1906 at Ormond Beach, Florida, Fred Mariott, driving a stock model, 1,600 pound Stanley Steamer, carrying a steam pressure of 1,300 pounds attained a speed of 197 miles per hour before the car flew to pieces. Mariott was thrown clear and was merely shaken up. This speed record stood until 1927, when it was broken by a four ton monster powered by two twelve cylinder airplane engines. A Stanley Steamer was once driven from Los Angeles to New York on $4.50 worth of fuel oil. 39

Milwaukee Steam Carriage 1897, oldest in Pioneer Village collection.

One of the oldest cars in existence is on display at the Harold Warp Pioneer Village Foundation. It is an 1897 Milwaukee Steam Carriage that cost $765.00 new, when Mr. Beirman drove it from Milwaukee to his home in Hastings, Nebraska. This is believed to be the only "Milwaukee" in existence. 40

Early motorcycles were more popular than horseless carriages.

Contrary to popular belief, the first vehicle powered by a four cycle engine was not a car; it was a motorcycle using hot-tube ignition, before electric ignition was developed. Developed in 1885 by Daimler of Germany, it was followed by Harley Davidson in 1900, with Indian, 1901, Curtiss, 1903 and Excelsior and Henderson motorcycles coming later. The world's best collection of motorcycles is believed to be at the Harold Warp Pioneer Village at Minden, Nebraska.   41

Minden, Neb. 68959

George B. Selden

Every car manufactured prior to 1911, paid Mr. Seldon 5% royalty except Henry Ford.

A New York attorney, George B. Selden, applied for a patent on a theoretical horseless carriage in 1876. Being an attorney, he kept his patent application open by making amendments until November 5, 1893. His basic automobile patent would run for seventeen years, although Seldon never built an automobile. That same year Duryea Brothers built the first successful gasoline powered horseless carriage. For the next seventeen years every car manufactured tacked a 2" x 4" plate on the dash acknowledging Selden's patent number and paid Selden five percent license fees for his theoretical automobile patent except Henry Ford, who finally broke Selden's patent in 1911, after many years of litigation. Selden had collected over a million dollars in royalties from other automobile manufacturers before Henry Ford proved Selden's patent invalid in 1911. During the five years the Ford/Selden patent case was in the courts, Henry Ford guaranteed his dealers that they would not have to pay Selden a patent fee.   42

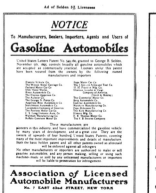

The identical Stanley twins were no fools. (also see #256)

The Stanley name went on their steamers after buying back their patents in 1905.

Charles E. Duryea

How Bill Smith's buggy became the Duryea.

J. Frank Duryea

Duryea at Pioneer Village.

The 1899 Mobile Steam Carriage was designed by the Stanley Brothers, but before they went into production, sold their patents, plant and all to Walker and Barber for $250,000.00. Stanley Brothers were no fools. They had previously designed Stanley tools and also a photo finishing process that they had sold to George Eastman for $800,000. 43

In 1905 the Stanley twin brothers bought back their Mobile Steam Carriage patents at a fraction of the $250,000 they were originally paid by Walker and Barber. They then commenced making Stanley Steamers. Both Steamers are on display at the Harold Warp Pioneer Village. 44

One April day in 1892, Charles Duryea walked into Bill Smith's buggy shop at 2 Park Street, Springfield, Massachussetts and said "I have invented a machine, when attached to a carriage will make it go without a horse. For the experiment I need an old buggy, which will not cost much." Bill Smith said, "I have a shed full of old buggies out back, take your pick." Duryea selected a used buggy with a top and Smith delivered it with his horse drawn livery wagon. Two weeks later, on April 19, 1892, the old buggy drew up in front of Smith's office door. It was an awesome sight with no horse in front of it. Charles Duryea sat with a steering bar in his hand, while sputtering sounds came from the gasoline engine under the seat. A patent was granted Charles Duryea for that horseless carriage, June 11, 1895 and it is now on display at the Smithsonian Institute in Washington, D.C., a gift of Inglis Uppercu in 1920. A production model, built by Charles and Frank Duryea in 1896, the oldest car registered in the State of Michigan as far back as 1932, was purchased by Harold Warp in 1955 from Joe Hughes of Pontiac, Michigan, for his Pioneer Village in Minden, Nebraska, now on display there. 45

Ransom Eli Olds

Ranny Olds, a blacksmith's son, in the 1890s, first made steam engines and later made gasoline engines in his dad's Lansing, Michigan, blacksmith shop. He put one of his gasoline engines under the seat of a buggy, to propel the first Oldsmobile in 1897.   46

Ransom Eli Olds, who built his first (steam powered) automobile in 1886 was considered "Father of the Automobile". He retired a millionaire the year Henry Ford started making Fords. They were both 40. The year was 1903.   47

Ranny Olds retired the year Henry started making Fords.

"Reo" Auto: In 1905 shortly after Ransom E. Olds sold his interest in his one cylinder Oldsmobile, he introduced the two cylinder "REO" using his initials. It sold for $675 and claimed 57 miles on a gallon of gasoline. The Reo Speed Wagon and Reo Flying Cloud sold well in the 1920s and early 1930s, but the depression years caused Reo to quit making cars in 1936.   48

Ranny couldn't stay retired.

Henry's dad didn't approve of Ford's "Quadricycle".

Henry Ford's first machine going by its own power he called a "quadricycle" because of its four wheels. When it was finished, and had been tested to make sure it would run, he invited a friend to ride out with him to his father's farm. Henry's father was a farmer, a believer in horses, a man of position in the neighborhood, a justice of the peace and a Baptist deacon. As Henry proudly drove through the farm gate to where his father and a neighbor were standing in the lot, they just stared-speechless. Every line in his father's face indicated shame and humiliation that Henry, a grown man, should still be playing with toys. The older man said never a word, only looked his displeasure. When Henry could endure his father's disdain no longer, he turned to his friend and said, "Come on, let's you and me get out of here." He drove back through his father's gate again and headed for Detroit.   49

Henry Ford designed the first (1902) Cadillac.

Henry Ford patented the first carburetor. When he was not satisfied with the one cylinder Cadillac that he designed in 1902, he sold his carburetor patent to his Cadillac backers for $1800 with the understanding they would not call their car "Ford". Henry Ford proceeded to make the identical car in 1903 except for a 2-cylinder engine under the seat and he never after that acknowledged patents, including George Selden's automobile patent of 1895. All other auto makers paid Selden a 5% royalty on each car they sold, until Henry Ford broke Selden's patent in 1911. See that first 1902 Cadillac, the identical 1903 Ford and also Selden's patent notice on all cars except Fords at the Harold Warp Pioneer Village at Minden in south central Nebraska. Both the Ford and the Cadillac sold for $850.

50

Minden, Neb. 68959

In 1902 Henry Ford wrote his brother "I can make $ racing but I can't make ¢ manufacturing." His first two ventures had failed. His third final and successful venture was financed with just $27,000, put up by friends.

Henry Ford failed twice before his successful third venture at age 40. His first venture used up $86,000 of his backer's money before he called it quits in 1899. In 1902, after spending $38,000 of other people's money designing the first one cylinder Cadillac car, he wrote his brothers: "I can make $ racing, but I can't make ¢ manufacturing." In 1903 Ford raised $27,000 among friends. Most of the money came from Alexander Malcomson, who had delivered coal to Mr. Ford. They each took 25½% of the stock. The Dodge Brothers agreed to furnish the chassis and each get 50 shares if Malcomson would guarantee the bill. Charles Bennett, Daisy Air Rifle president, took 50 shares. They put a 2-cylinder engine in the same chassis as used for the 1902 1-cylinder Cadillac Ford had designed in 1902. He offered his 2-cylinder Model A ford for $850.00 and was on his way to undreamed of wealth.

51

Minden, Neb. 68959

Henry Ford's old "999" racer was found in a California junk yard.

Childe Harold Wills was the man who helped Henry Ford build his now famous "Old 999" racer, in a little unheated shop at 81 Park Place in Detroit. Old 999 was destined to beat all racing comers and helped to establish the Ford Motor Company in its third and successful venture with the introduction of the "Model A" in 1903. "Old 999" was built on 2" x 6" wood stringers and was resurrected from a California junk yard many years later.   52

Henry Ford wanted to find out whether the Horseless Carriage was a poor man's necessity or a rich man's toy, so he offered these two choices in 1906 and 1907. The Model N at $600 went on to become the Model T and the Model K was discontinued in 1907. Both cars are side by side at the Harold Warp Pioneer Village. These ads appeared in 1907.   53

Henry Ford

Was the horseless carriage a rich man's toy or a poor man's necessity?

500 Fascinating Facts

By 1927, half the cars on the road were Model T Fords, launched in 1908. By 1925 Fords cost $290.

The Model T Ford was introduced in the fall of 1908, for $850, but the price was progressively cut until in 1925 a Ford Roadster could be bought for $260. It was one of the first cars to have electric lights and ignition furnished by an ingenious magneto which was part of the flywheel. It had no storage battery. It also had as standard equipment a top, windshield, and fenders. Prior to 1910 they were "extras" on most horseless carriages. More than 15 million Model T Fords were made between October 1908 and May 1927. Over half the cars on the road were then Model T's, that averaged 30 to 35 miles on a gallon of gas and it usually took a quart of oil with each five gallons of gasoline. (The spark plugs screwed together for easy carbon removal.) 54

In 1919, Henry Ford bought out all his partners for $105,820,894.

Henry Ford owned 58% of the Ford Motor Company in July, 1919. He then agreed to pay other stockholders $25,500 per share for their stock, costing Ford $105,820,894 to own the Ford Motor Company. He had to borrow $60,000,000 that he was not in the habit of doing. 55

Ford's left hand steering came about conveniently when he turned the engine around.

Early cars were driven from the right, carried over from the "horse and buggy." In fact, some early cars even had a whip socket also on the right. Henry Ford moved the steering wheel to the left side when he introduced the Model T in October 1908. The writer is of the opinion that Henry Ford put the wheel on the left merely for convenience when he turned the engine around to accommodate the magneto which was fastened to the flywheel in the planetary clutch housing. A four cylinder one piece block replaced the two copper-jacketed sections. Henry Ford stated, however, that he believed if the wheel were on the left, the right hand could more easily handle the important work of steering while the left hand operated the hand levers. Drivers could also see approaching cars better. By 1910 the right-hand drive was obsolete, due to the spontaneous acceptance of Henry Ford's Model T that was first with left side steering. 56

Henry Ford

Edsel Ford's death, before his dad, created quite a problem for Henry Ford.

Edsel Ford

Henry Ford II

Henry Ford's assembly line.

Splash aprons came before windshields.

For half a century it was not known what Ford's annual sales were, how much his profits nor his net worth, for the Ford Corporation was strictly a family affair. Ironically, when old Henry's son, Edsel, happened to die before his dad, it became necessary to place a large share of the family fortune in an irrevocable trust, called "The Ford Foundation," to save the Ford Motor Co. from being dissolved to pay inheritance taxes. Fortunately the three grandsons were able to revive the dying Ford dynasty. In 1956, nine years after Henry Ford's death at 83, the Ford Foundation made a deal with Ford heirs to give the stock in trust voting rights. They didn't want "all their eggs in one basket." By late 1959 The Ford Foundation had sold approximately one third of its 90% holdings of Ford stock for nearly a billion dollars. Ironically, when this Ford stock was placed on the open market it exposed to the public the one thing old Henry had always kept secret: annual sales, profits and net worth of the gigantic Ford Motor Company. Ford Foundation continued to sell $200 million to $400 million in Ford stock each year until their portfolio contained no Ford stock by 1975. Ironically, there was a time when the Ford Foundation was accused of sponsoring communistic activities.   57

Ford Production Data:

1903 -	1,708	1912 -	78,440
1905 -	1,695	1913 -	168,220
1906 -	1,599	1914 -	248,307
1907 -	8,423	1915 -	533,921
1908 -	6,398	1920 -	945,850
1909 -	10,607	1923 -	2,055,309
1910 -	18,664	1927 -	380,741
1911 -	34,528		

58

A "splash apron" was offered as an extra on most Horseless Carriages before 1910. This was before windshields were thought of. It was made of black oil cloth with a small "celluloid" window sewed in for the driver to see through. It was fastened with snaps all around the front portion of the car.   59

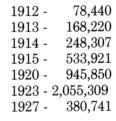

Facts About the Model T Ford — 1908-1927:

1908 - First Model T sold in October for $850. (Extras - side curtains, $60, windshield.)

1911 - Wooden bodies discontinued.

1912 - Doors could be purchased as accessories.

1913 - First front right door. No left front touring car door, only a door design on the body.

1913 - Leatherette replaced some leather in Fords.

1914 - Cherry-wood dash board replaced with steel.

1914 - Coupelet introduced, first Ford closed car.

1915 - Last straight back fenders. Acetylene lights and bulb horn replaced with electric.

1916 - Brass radiator discontinued. Rounded fenders and rounded body introduced.

1920 - Kerosene buggy lights eliminated on dash.

1923 - Sloping windshield introduced.

1926 - Kerosene tail lamp replaced with electric. Fifteen million Fords were made from 1908 to 1927 with same dies (over half of the cars on the roads in 1927 were Fords). 60

The Ford chasis never changed; only body improvements evolved.

The Model T Ford touring car never had a front left door.

All car bodies were made of wood prior to 1912, when Henry Ford introduced a steel body on the Model T. It had doors for the back seat but none in front and it still had a cherry wood dashboard until 1916. 61

The customer could have any color, as long as it was black.

In 1926 Henry Ford stated "The customer can have any color he wants as long as it is black,* but I will never change the Model T motor." A year later, in June 1927 Ford closed for retooling because people had commenced preferring the 3-speed gearshift Chevrolet, available in colors. *Ford dipped his car bodies in molten asphalt then baked it to get the black color. He made over 2 million Model Ts in 1926. 62

Dodge brothers made Henry Ford's Model T engines and also the chasis for first few years.

Horace and John Dodge got their big boost in the automobile business by accepting contract work from Henry Ford. They made Ford's engines for several years, resulting in $ millions in profits. They brought out their own four cylinder car in 1914 with the first "all steel" body, which was an immediate success. The touring car sold for about $800.00. In 1917 Dodge Brothers introduced a "closed car" for $1,185.00 that had a single door on each side. 63

Horace Dodge

John Dodge

In 1919, Henry Ford was ordered to pay Dodge brothers $19,275,325; retained profits.

In 1916 the Dodge Brothers sued Henry Ford for their share of Ford's retained profits. In February 1919 the Michigan Supreme Court ordered Ford to pay the Dodge Brothers $19,275,325 for their share of profits on their 50 shares of stock in Ford Motor Co. Then in July 1919 he purchased the Dodge Brothers' 50 shares of stock for $625,000,000, that had cost them nothing when they commenced making the complete Ford chassis in 1903. 64

Sears tried selling cars twice.

Sears Roebuck failed twice in selling cars. They introduced the "Sears Motor Buggy" in 1906 for $370. The top and fenders were $25 extra. They put it on the back cover of their catalog in 1909 and quit selling their motor buggy in 1912. It was a high wheeler with solid rubber tires and had tiller steering. Sears sold it to the Lincoln Motor Car Co. 65

Kaiser-Frazer made "Alstate" cars, sold only in Sears stores (1952-1953).

Although the "Sears Motor Buggy" was featured on their back cover in 1909 and was discontinued in 1912, this did not prevent Sears from trying again in 1952. When they commenced marketing the Allstate, made by Kaiser-Frazer, it was sold only in their stores. They did not put it in their catalog this time. Sears sold 1566 Allstates in 1952 and 797 in 1953, the year it was discontinued. The 4-cylinder Allstate sold for $1544 and the 6-cylinder for $1692. See both Sears cars among 350 others at the Harold Warp Pioneer Village Foundation at Minden in south central Nebraska. 66

David Buick

Dave invented the trip toilet and vitrous enamel bath tub before "Buick" gasoline engines and cars.

David Buick, before he made cars, invented the trip toilet and the vitreous enamel bathtub. In the late 1890s he also started making gasoline engines, one of which he placed in a buggy to propel the first Buick automobile. Both Ranny Olds and Dave Buick's gasoline engines, were designed to pull washing machines and windmill pump jacks before they put them in autos. David Dunbar Buick died a poor man in 1929, while employed by a trade school, although he had become wealthy with his invention of the trip toilet and his perfection of the process for making baked enamel bathtubs. He lost his fortune in development of the car that bears his name and sold out to Wm. Durant in 1905, who started the giant General Motors Corporation with Buick. 67

Oldest Buick in existance is at Pioneer Village, Minden, Neb.

The oldest Buick in existence is at the Harold Warp Pioneer Village, Minden, Nebraska. Made in 1905, it was purchased from Alton Walker, Pebble Beach, California by Harold Warp in 1958. It sold new for $1,000.00. 68

Billy Durant, 1908

Henry Ford agreed to sell out to him, but Ford wanted gold.

Billie Durant was a carriage maker in Flint, Michigan in the year 1900. He started General Motors Company by capitalizing Buick in 1905 for $10,000,000. By 1908 he had added Oldsmobile, Cadillac, Northway and Oakland to the combine. (Henry Ford also agreed to sell out to him for $8,000,000, but wanted 2,000,000 of it in gold, but Billie Durant never dealt in cash. 69

"Durant's folly" netted stockholders $10 1/2 million in 1910, the same year bankers kicked Billy out.

Detroit called the General Motors combine "Durant's Folly", but by 1910 G.M. sold $34 million worth of cars and netted stockholders $10.5 million profit. Nevertheless, Billie Durant could not meet payments he had promised the car manufacturers, so New York bankers took over General Motors in 1910 and they kicked him out. 70

$690 "Little" Chevrolet, 1911

Kicked out of General Motors, Billy Durant bought out Chevrolet.

When Billie Durant was fired as manager of General Motors in 1910, he went to his old racing friend, Louis Chevrolet, who was having William Little (Durant's former Buick factory manager) build him a racing car. Billie Durant bought the factory with financial help from the DuPonts and proceeded to have Bill Little design a car similar to the Voituretto that he had seen in France, to compete with Ford's Model T.   71

In 1918, Billy Durant told General Motors stockholder's meeting "Gentlemen I own this company" only to lose it again in 1920 to the DuPonts.

In 1911 Billie Durant introduced the huge 6-cylinder Chevrolet for $3000 and the "Little" car for $690. By 1913 he had dropped the huge 6-cylinder Chevrolet and renamed Bill Little's car the Baby Grand Chevrolet, that later became the 490 Chevrolet ($490), that sold 50,000 copies in 1916. He then offered five shares of Chevrolet stock for each share of General Motors and by September 16, 1918 he walked into the General Motors stockholders meeting and calmly told them: "Gentlemen, I control this company," which indeed he did, with the help of the DuPont family who had made huge profits manufacturing explosives during World War I. He proceeded to buy up Frigidaire, Delco Electric Co., Hyatt Bearing Co., and Fisher Body Co., which ran him out of cash again and this time DuPont's took over General Motors in 1920. They kicked out Billie Durant and put in Alfred P. Sloan who then ran GM for many years.   72

Baby Grand Chevrolet

In 1922, when Billie Durant had lost control of General Motors to the DuPont family the second and last time, he introduced the "Durant", the "Star" and then in 1923 the "Flint" cars, but this time he was unable to compete with DuPont's huge General Motors Co. that he had fathered. In 1926 he went bankrupt. He moved back to Flint, Michigan and was able to get together enough money to start a bowling alley, but the spark of genius was gone and he died broke in 1947 at the age of 85. Just eight people followed his hearse to

The "Durant", "Flint" and "Star" flopped.

Although he had put millions of people to work, only 8 people followed Billy Durant to the cemetery when he died.

the cemetery, Mike Hamady, a Flint, Michigan storekeeper among them. During all of his years with General Motors Corp., Billie Durant, who put millions of people to work, never drew a cent in salary or expenses.   73

Do people resent change? Pioneer car makers found it difficult to separate the idea of the horseless carriage from the horse and carriage. Early automobiles had carriage wheels, dashboards, whip sockets, side lamps and tillers instead of a steering wheel. To preserve the entire shape of horse and buggy one A. Smith actually used a horse's head on his horseless carriage.   74

More proof that people resent change.

Back in the early days of the automobile, in Urbana, Ohio, automobile speeds were limited to 4 miles per hour, and the operator was required to sound a gong or bell within 50 feet of a crossing, to be kept sounding until after the crossing was passed. The city of Mitchell, South Dakota passed an ordinance forbidding any motor vehicle to enter the city limits. New York State required that a "mature person" be sent at least 1/8 mile ahead to warn horse-drawn vehicles of the approach of an automobile. In 1890, a New York State law prohibited steam engines on public right-of-ways unless a man be seated up forward to prevent run-away horses. By 1905 automobiles had become such a nuisance in Nebraska that the State Legislature passed a law requiring the operator of a Horseless Carriage to halt on the highway until the driver of any frightened horse could get past.   75

Laws to prevent progress.

Both horses and humans wanted horseless carriages to resemble carriages.

Early autos resembled buggies for two reasons. Folks refused to buy them if they did not bear familiar lines – and horses refused to be seen on the same road with them for the same reason.   76

Horseless carriages considered nuisances.

Who had the right-of-way? The first horseless carriages were considered nuisances and many states passed laws requiring operators to pull off the road to allow the driver of any frightened horse to go past. 77

Buggy whips, contrary to reports, were not carried by the drivers of horseless carriages to beat off vengeful horses. They were used to chase cows and dogs off the roads. Also rural school kids would hang on to one of the back wheels of the rural mail carrier's one-cylinder car, to stop it. (As the writer recalls) 78

Early cars had buggy whip holders.

A broken jaw led to the invention of the self-starter. When Byron Carter, inventor of the Carter car, died of complications due to a jaw broken by a backlashing crank, his death prompted Charles Kettering to develop the self-starter in 1912. 79

A broken jaw sparked the self-starter.

The first horseless carriage race, Decoration Day, 1896, was sponsored by the Cosmopolitan magazine. It offered a $3,000.00 first prize. In this fifty-two mile race from Cosmopolitan's offices in New York to their printing plant in Irvington, New Jersey, six horseless carriages entered. A Duryea won the fifty-two mile race in seven hours, thirteen minutes, averaging six and three-quarter miles per hour. 80

6 3/4 M.P.H. won first auto race.

With the clogged roads that we have today, will we return to yesteryear's travel? The average speed of traffic in New York City in 1907 – when vehicles were horse-drawn – was 11.5 miles per hour. In 1966, motor vehicles averaged 8.5 miles per hour. America's first auto race Thanksgiving Day, 1895, from Chicago to Evanston and back (52 miles) averaged 5 mph. 81

Traffic jams not new.

It was simply the script type of a schoolboy who made calling cards.

Probably one of the most famous insignias is the Ford automobile trademark. It was not developed by a renowned artist or designer; but was the handiwork of C.H. Wills, Henry Ford's helper. In 1904, he went home and set up the one word: FORD, from a font of script type he had made calling cards with as a school boy.   82

The Chevrolet design came from a French hotel wall.

The Chevrolet name plate design originated with a piece of wallpaper torn from the wall of a French hotel room in which Billie Durant stayed one night in 1908.   83

Cadillac emblem, coat of arms of founder of Detroit.

"Cadillac": Named after the founder of Detroit, Michigan, Le Sieur Antoine de la Mothe Cadillac and the crest was his coat of arms.   84

Named for the daughter of Daimler's distributor.

"Mercedes". In 1901 Gottlieb Daimler, a German car manufacturer, named a 28 horsepower, 4-cylinder model "Mercedes" after the daughter of his sole distributor in France, Belgium, Austria, and the United States, Emile Jellinek. In 1926 Gottlieb Daimler and Karl Benz merged to form the Mercedes-Benz Corporation.   85

BMW chose a three bladed propellor.

"BMW": Began as a aeronautical company. The circular blue and white emblem represented a spinning propeller.   86

During the 1970s new features offered in cars were: emission control, radial tires, disc brakes, 3 point safety belts, anti-roll bars, fuel injection, electronic engine controls and anti-lock brakes. In the 1980s: talking dash-boards, video panels, oddly placed controls, anti-theft systems, four wheel steering and computer controlled suspension.   87

500 Fascinating Facts

Carbide lights made it possible to drive at night.

The first horseless carriages were daylight travelers until John G. Marshall, Niagara Falls, N.Y., gave them carbide eyes in 1896. Fred Avery, in 1907. successfully compressed gas into a tank he named "Prest-O-Lite" to replace the messy water soaked carbide carried in a tank on the running board. In 1912 Chas. Kettering put the first electric self starter and electric lights on the 1912 Cadillac car. 88

The "snitching post" was the timely name given to the first parking meters when they replaced the old western hitching posts on Oklahoma City streets in 1935. The nation's first parking meters — 150 of them — were the brainchild of the late Carl Magee, attorney and newspaper editor. He dreamed up the idea as a device to increase the turnover in parking space on busy streets. Then a mechanical engineer from Ohio named Gerald H. Hale developed the clock-operated meter and joined with Magee as a partner. By 1980 there were 1,650,000 parking meters in 4057 U.S. cities that took in $252 million annually, with an average take of $63 per meter. 89

Invented to increase shopping in downtown Oklahoma City.

Albert Champion and R.E. Olds had something in common. Champion spark plugs were made by the Albert Champion Company of Flint, Michigan in 1908. In 1916 after selling out "Champion", he used his initials to start "AC" Spark Plugs, just as R.E. Olds had done in 1905 to start REO Auto Mfg. Co. 90

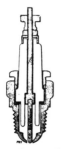

Ranny E. Olds and Albert Champion had something in common.

In the early 1900s auto fenders were called dust guards and were sold as extras that fit any auto. 91

Dust guards cost extra on horseless carriages.

The bumper on today's car is following running boards and rumble seats to oblivion. Back in 1915, the bumper was considered optional equipment, and it really served a purpose. 92

Bumpers really were bumpers, back then.

At the turn of the century there were more steam and electric horseless carriages sold than gasoline buggies. The Stanley Brothers made their first practical steam car in 1898 and as these identical twins, 47 years old, proceeded to drive around Newton, Massachusetts in it, they took orders to "mass produce" a hundred of them. The Stanley Brothers, F. E. and F. O., were no fools. They had developed Stanley tools and a photographic process that they sold to George Eastman for approximately $800,000. While in Europe in 1896, F. O. saw a steam automobile. He casually said he thought he could build a better one and he did, with the aid of his twin brother, F. E. In November 1898, upon winning a race at Charles River Park, averaging 27.4 M.P.H., there were 100 of the 5,000 spectators that ordered Stanley Steamers on the spot. To fill the orders they bought a bicycle shop and started making them. The Stanley Brothers weren't particularly interested in manufacturing at the time, and before the 100 steam cars were completed they sold out in 1899, to Walker and Barber for $250,000.00, which included patents and unfinished cars, but they were to continue on as managers with the understanding they would not compete for a period of two years. The steamers under construction were named "Locomobile". The partners couldn't agree, so Walker commenced making "Mobile Steamers," with F. O. Stanley as manager and Barber continued to make Locomobiles with F. E. Stanley as manager. For the next year or more F. O. and F. E. found themselves in the odd position of being competitors. The Stanley Brothers did not like the setup, so they both resigned and started building an improved Stanley Steamer when their two year agreement not to compete was up. In 1905 the Stanley Brothers bought their patents back at a fraction of what they originally sold them for and continued to make the Stanley Steamer until the mid-twenties. It was the leading steamer. The Stanley Brothers retired in 1917 and the last Stanley Steamer was made in 1926. F. E. was killed in an accident while driving one of his own cars in 1918 and F. O. died of heart trouble in 1940.

The Stanley twins were forced to be competitors in 1903, but they corrected that in 1905.

F.O. Stanley

F.E. was accidentally killed in 1918 but F.O. lived until 1940.

93

R.E. Olds

His dad didn't want him wasting time on "that crazy contraption" when Ranny made his first 3-wheel steam carriage.

In 1884 "Olds & Son" introduced a steam engine fired by a waste product called "gasoline" and made 2000 of them in the next three years.

In 1896 several wealthy men wanted to give Ranny Olds orders for gasoline powered carriages, like the one he was driving around Lansing, Michigan.

At the tender age of 20 "Ranny" Olds had transformed his father's Lansing, Michigan blacksmith shop into a factory for making small steam engines of his own design in 1884. It was fired by a highly explosive waste product called gasoline that could not even be dumped into streams which was a by-product of the new miracle fuel, kerosene. His compact little steam engine was designed for pulling printing presses and butcher's sausage grinders. More than 2,000 were sold in the next three years by "R. E. Olds and Son." In 1886, when "Ranny" was 22, he made his first horseless carriage, a three wheeled steam powered carriage. It was designed and built by Ranny Olds in spare time, with his own money, for his father did not want him wasting valuable day time on that "crazy contraption." It became the first horseless carriage ever to roll along a Michigan road. Four years later, in 1890, he completed his second steam carriage that could "easily do 10 miles per hour," got a nice write-up on it in the May 1892 Scientific American and sold it in 1893 for $400 to a man in Bombay, India. This was the first horseless carriage ever sold and shipped out of the United States.

In 1893 the Olds Gasoline Engine Works was incorporated for $30,000 with R. E. Olds as president and general manager, after his aging father, Pliny, conceded to become a stockholder. The company met with much success in producing gasoline engines designed by "Ranney". In 1896 R.E. Olds built his first gasoline engine powered carriage. Several wealthy men were impressed by the way Ranny Olds drove his horseless carriage around Lansing, Michigan, and in 1897 induced him to become manager of a corporation they formed known as the Olds Motor Vehicle Company, capitalized at $50,000 with $5,00 cash paid in. Olds ordered enough material to produce six cars and four of them were made in 1897. One went to Tennessee, one to California, and two to Michigan. One of these four eventually found its way to the Smithsonian Institute in Washington, D.C., where it is on display today.

In 1899 the Olds Gasoline Engine Company and Olds Motor Vehicle Company merged to form the Olds Motor Works. The paid in capital was

Ranny Olds got up one night at 3 o'clock and sketched the little 700 pound curved dash Olds, costing $680. It was an immediate success when he introduced it in 1901. In January 1904 he sold out a millionaire, the same year Henry commenced making Fords.

REO ₋₄₋Seat₋₋ $675
Runabout

Ranny couldn't stay retired. In August, 1904 he decided to introduce the "REO" using his initials, as suggested by one of his backers.

$350,000 and R.E. Olds received $50,000 for his interest in the Olds Gasoline Engine Company. He was put in charge, but not in control. Due to labor troubles in Lansing they decided to make the Olds cars in Detroit, where a new factory was erected on a 4½ acre site near the Belle Isle bridge in 1899. This three story building was the first ever constructed for the sole production of automobiles. The 1899 Oldsmobile that sold for $1,350 did not meet with much success. While "Ranny" was unable to sleep one night, trying to solve the problem, the idea for an entirely different car came to him. At three o'clock in the morning he got up and commenced sketching the curved dash Olds, that was to weigh only 700 pounds. A few of them were produced in 1900. It met with such success that the first assembly line for making Oldsmobiles was set up in the new Detroit plant in January 1901 to fill the orders. Fire destroyed the Detroit plant in the spring of 1901, just as the country's first mass production of cars was getting underway. Immediately upon hearing of the Detroit fire, the city of Lansing offered Olds the former State Fair Grounds, consisting of 52 acres, at no cost, on which several old buildings were available on the grounds to assure immediate production. The "Olds" board lost no time in taking advantage of Lansing's generous offer and surprisingly, before 1901 was over, 400 curved dash Oldsmobiles had been turned out on the Lansing fairgrounds. During the first full year of production in 1902, after moving back to Lansing, the Olds Motor Works actually delivered 3,750 curved dash, one cylinder Oldsmobiles and in 1903 they produced 5,000. The car sold for $650 cash. In January 1904 R. E. Olds disagreed with the directors who wanted to produce a larger car and he resigned from the Olds Motor Works, a millionaire. This was 22 years after making his first horseless car-automobiles. They were both 40 years old.

Hearing of Ranny's resignation from the Olds Motor Works, a group of ten Lansing Men, in August 1904, induced Olds to accept $260,000 worth of stock free, "providing he accepts management of the company," in which they put up $240,000 among them. One of the men suggested

In 1908 R.E. Olds and his friends refused to sell REO for $4 million to Wm. C. Durant, who was then putting together General Motors Corp. Ranny continued on as chairman of REO until 1937 and before he died in 1951, had a yacht built with no flush toilets so guests wouldn't stay aboard too long.

naming the new $500,000 corporation "Reo", taking R.E. Olds initials. The first year's sales totaled $1,375,000 enabling them to pay off the $260,000 stock given Olds and still pay a 10% dividend. In 1908, just four years after "Ranny" Olds pulled out of Oldsmobile and the year Wm. C. Durant acquired control of Oldsmobile at a reasonable price "just to get the name," R.E. Olds and his friends refused to sell to Durant the Reo for $4,000,000. The company continued to be highly successful under R.E. Olds' guidance until he retired as chairman of the board in 1937. He died in 1951 a very wealthy man, having designed several yachts himself, that he had built, one of which had no flush toilets for guests to clog up carelessly with refuse. 94

HAROLD WARP
PIONEER VILLAGE
Minden, Neb. 68959 FOUNDATION

Model N Ford, 1906

This Model K went a mile a minute.

In 1906 Henry Ford wanted to find out if the horseless carriage was a rich man's toy or a poor man's necessity. The Model T was the answer. (See fact #53)

When Henry Ford started making cars in his third venture, in 1903, the horseless carriage was then considered a rich man's toy. Ford was determined to find out, for R. E. Olds had fairly good acceptance with his curved dash "Olds" before he sold out and was currently doing alright with his little $675 "Reo." So Henry proceeded to design a big six cylinder Ford, (costing $3,000.00) that would make the one cylinder Cadillac look sick, (which he had designed in 1902). He also designed the little Model "N" Ford with four cylinders, developing 15 H.P., to compete with the little one cylinder curved dash Olds. Henry's "N" Ford had battery ignition, sported a water pump, forced oil feed and kerosene lights. It had an open planetary clutch and torsion tube drive and sold for $600. The little Model "N" was an immediate success at the New York Auto Show in January, 1906, even though it had no engine under the sealed down hood, that they did not have ready when the show opened. Ford told the folks at the show that what was under that Model "N" hood was a secret and indeed it was. He dropped the Big Six when he found out that folks no longer considered the horseless carriage a toy. He made 2,500 Model "N" Fords in 1906 and was on his way to undreamed of wealth. 95

When Henry put the magneto in the fly wheel on the Model T, he had to turn the engine around, which necessitated moving the steering wheel from the right side to the left side.

So successful was Henry Ford with his little Model "N", and so unsuccessful with his big 1906 Model K, that late in 1906 he started designing the Model T, which was really only a refinement of the Model N, with the planetary clutch enclosed. He replaced the two copper-jacketed engine sections with a solid 4-cylinder block. The motor was turned around so a magneto could be attached to the flywheel inside the planetary clutch housing. The water pump and oil pressure systems were eliminated. Tire sizes were increased from 28″ x 3″ to 30″ x 3″. The Model T could carry five people, however, and carried them so well for the next 19 years, with no major changes, that it ran Old Dobbin right off the road. 96

In 1924 the Model T sold for $290. He made a Ford every 5 seconds and half the cars on the road were Fords.

The Model "T" Ford was so durable that in March 1927, nineteen years after introduction in 1908, there were still 11,325,521 Ford "tin lizzies" still registered in the US; of the 15 million made.

After having proved to himself with the little Model N that a car was to become the poor man's necessity, Henry Ford introduced the Model T in September 1908 for $850, at a time when most cars were selling for $2,000 or more. Side curtains were $60 extra, a brass windshield $35 extra and carbide head lights were $27 extra. It was destined to revolutionize man's mode of travel. For the first ten years after introducing the Model T Henry Ford nearly doubled production every year, paying for plant expansion out of profits. He advocated assembly line production, shorter working hours and higher hourly wages. During the 19 years that he made the Model T, Ford turned out 15,500,000 cars, (two every ten seconds in 1923), on an original capitalization of $28,000. By 1924 the Ford sold for $290. He continued to sell the Model "T", with only slight body changes, until 1927. During these 19 years no major changes were made in the motor or chassis and over half the cars on country roads were Fords. It is estimated that over 5,000 gadgets were made to fit the Model T and 10,000 jokes helped sell it. 97

Walter P. Chrysler

Born in Wamego, Kansas in 1875, he went from railroad mechanic to head of Buick, to vice president of General Motors and retired a millionaire at age 45 in 1919.

Mechanical toy banks fascinated Walter Chrysler. When they failed to flip the penny into the slot he'd fix them. When he died in 1940 he had one of the largest collections of mechanical banks in the world. Although Walter had never really placed much value on them, when sold by his estate, they brought over $30,000.00. Walter P. Chrysler was born April 2, 1875 at Wamego, Kansas, the son of a K. P. railroad engineer. When he was old enough to work, he got a job sweeping up around the railroad yards. In his spare time he made a set of tools, graduating to a master railroad machinist by the time he was 33 in 1908. (He had married his boyhood sweetheart in 1901.) That year he was made head machinist for the C. G. W. Ry. of Chicago. It so happened that 1908 was the year the Auto Show was held in Chicago, where Henry Ford's Model T was introduced and it was also the year that Billy Durant put together the gigantic General Motors Corporation. At that show Walter bought a Locomobile Steamer.

In 1910 he quit his job as superintendent at the American Locomotive Company's Pittsburgh works at $12,000 per year to accept a job with Billy Durant at only $6,000 per year, to work under Chas. W. Nash, then Works Manager for Buick. By then one million cars had been sold in the United States. Within five years Buick was paying Walter half a million dollars a year, as president, and making over 500 cars a day. In 1919 Walter Chrysler was made Vice-President of General Motors, directly under the financial genius, Billy Durant. Within the year, however, he had disagreements with General Motors (during their financial shakeup) and retired a millionaire at 45. His retirement lasted less than a year.

Some farmers made money on their mud holes.

In 1920 a group of bankers induced him to try and get Willys-Overland back on its feet, which he succeeded in doing in two years. For this he was paid a million dollars a year. While at Willys-Overland he became interested in trying to build a high compression engine capable of producing more power with less gas. In 1923 he hired three assistants, Zeder, Skelton and Breer. They moved into the abandoned Chalmers plant to try and build just such a car. Their experiments were conducted on an old Maxwell. The old rejuvenated Maxwell was renamed the "Chrysler 6" and they intended to show it at the New York Auto Show in January 1924, but were refused space in Grand Central Palace. Walter proceeded to rent the lobby of the Commodore Hotel and the car's sleek appearance stole the show. That year they built 32,000 Chrysler Sixes.

In 1924 Walter Chrysler was refused space at the New York Auto Show with a rejuvenated Maxwell car that he renamed the "Chrysler 6", with a new high compression engine that used less gasoline. He rented the lobby of the Commodore Hotel and stole the show with the car's sleek lines.

In 1925 he took over the Maxwell Motor Company, whose stock he had been accumulating, and he had 3,800 dealers signed up to sell the new high compression Chrysler. In 1926 Walter offered four models of Chryslers and their sales climbed to 1,250 cars per day. By 1927 Chrysler had climbed to fourth place in auto sales. In 1928, when auto production in the U.S. had climbed to over 4,000,000 per year, Chrysler acquired the Dodge Brothers Corporation from the banking house of Dillon Read & Company, who had purchased it in 1920 from the heirs of the Dodge boys for $146,000,000, the year both Dodge brothers died. Later that same year (1928) Walter Chrysler introduced the "DeSoto" and the "Plymouth" that he had been perfecting for two years, but they did not actually get into production on the Plymouth until March 1929. In 1934 the "Airflow" DeSoto and Chrysler were introduced but they were so far ahead of time in stream-lining that they were a flop.

The airflow DeSoto came out 20 years too soon.

Walter Chrysler proceeded to take over "Dodge" in 1928, the same year he introduced "DeSoto" and "Plymouth". He continued to head "Chrysler" until his death in 1940, age 65, a multi-millionaire.

Walter Chrysler had led an active life, was getting old and consequently in the late Thirties assigned more and more responsibility to his close friend and associate, K.T. Keller, who had joined Chrysler in 1926. After two years of illness Walter P. Chrysler, the man who tinkered his way to fame and fortune, died a multi-millionaire on August 18, 1940, at 65.   98

HAROLD WARP
PIONEER VILLAGE FOUNDATION
Minden, Neb. 68959

Louis Chevrolet, who was winning races against Barny Oldfield, driving Henry Ford's handlebar steering 999, caught the eye of Billy Durant, who was putting together General Motors.

Louis Chevrolet was a Christmas present to his Swiss parents, for he was born on December 25, 1878 in La Chaux de Fonda, Switzerland. As a young man, he ran a bicycle shop in Burgundy, France. Before Louis left France for America he designed a wine pump, that was not as sensational as the many cars he designed and built after he and his brothers, Gaston and Arthur, arrived in the United States in 1900. Louis took a job with Hollander, a foreign car dealer in New York, who in time introduced him to Alfred Reeves, a race promoter looking for a driver to try and beat Barney Oldfield, then winning all the races with Henry Ford's handlebar steering "999". Louis agreed to race against Barney. With a 90 FIAT Louis Chevrolet beat Barney Oldfield in three races during 1905. That same year he smashed up two FIAT racers by colliding with telephone poles on the turns. He was indeed a wild driver, as well as a good mechanic, and he caught the eye of another promoter, William Crapo Durant, who operated on the theory that $1,000 was the smallest unit of U.S. currency. In 1908, after interviewing both Louis and his brother, Arthur, Durant hired them both. He gave Arthur a job as his private chauffeur and put Louis in a Buick racer to help promote his "General Motors" he was trying to put together, with Buick as "backbone" of the corporation. Louis won several races in 1908, including the Vanderbilt Cup Race, with a stock 30 H.P. Buick. Louis Chevrolet went on to win the Yorick Trophy in 1909 and he was leading in the 1910 Vanderbilt Cup Race when his steering gear failed, killing the mechanic riding with him but Louis was unhurt. His brother Arthur ran in the same "Buick team" that year.

Billy Durant put Louis Chevrolet in a Buick racer to help promote General Motors.

While Chevrolet was racing with the Buick, Durant was so busy buying up auto companies right and left that he over-extended himself. (Henry Ford agreed to sell for $8 million with $2 million down and the balance later but he wanted it all in GOLD so that deal fell through because Billy Durant dealt only in stocks.) On November 15, 1910, the New York bankers closed in on Will Durant and kicked him out. Billy Durant did not go out of General Motors destitute. He told Louis Chevrolet and Wm. H. Little, his former Buick factory manager,

$690 "Little" Chevrolet, 1911

When Billy Durant got kicked out of General Motors by bankers in 1910, he went to Bill Little and Louis Chevrolet and asked them to build him a small car heavy enough to bounce over the rough roads, which they did, and called it "Little", for $690.

The big 6-cylinder, $2150 "Chevrolet" was a flop, but the "Little" wasn't, so in 1913 Billy Durant changed the name to "Baby Grand Chevrolet" at $680 and sales soared, but in 1914 Louis Chevrolet and Billy Durant had a spat and Louis quit and went back to racing on his own.

Baby Grand Chevrolet

"we're going to need a car," so Chevrolet and Little, (then building racing engines as a side line) loyal to their former employer, proposed to design a small car along the lines of the French Voituretto to compete with the Model T Ford. Durant thought it a good idea but he asked them to build it heavier, so it would bounce over country roads. They proceeded to design a small, cheap "LITTLE" 4-cylinder car that sold for $690, named after Wm. H. Little. (The LITTLE car was discontinued in 1915.) During 1911 Louis was also working on a Big Six, 5-passenger car in a loft on Detroit's Grand River Avenue, that Durant incorporated as the Chevrolet Motor Company on November 3, 1911. It was priced at $2,150. Durant used Chevrolet's name on the car because it bore the name of a famous race driver (as did other cars of the day) and besides, it had a musical sound and suggested foreign origin. The $2150 Chevrolet was a mediocre success, and 2,999 units were sold in 1912 but the market for a big car was limited. Louis was a principal in the Chevrolet company, and arthur and Gaston were also stockholders. The "Little" hadn't taken much business from Ford's Model T and though the name "Chevrolet" was the magic that had sold the big cars, that market was limited, so Durant decided to bring out the "Baby Grand" Chevrolet at $680 and the "Royal Mail" at $750. From mid 1913 thru 1914 sales jumped to 6,243. This was the first time Durant used the now famous Chevrolet insignia that he copied from a piece of wall paper in France in 1908. During the next two years, Durant sold 16,000 cars and made a profit of $1,300. New models poured out, all with overhead valves; such successes as the Amesbury Special and the "490". But Louis Chevrolet wasn't convinced that the company's future was very bright, and in 1913, after a minor dispute with Durant, he dropped out. Durant bought up his interest in 1914 and Louis went off on his own. He went back to doing what he liked best, racing, for the rest of his life. He proceeded to design and build the "Monroe Special" that his brother Gaston won the 1920 Indianapolis race with, the Frontenac Special that won in 1921, and his 16-valve Fronty-Fords that subsequently won several Indianapolis races as the years rolled by.

Gaston Chevrolet was killed in 1920, driving a Monroe at the Los Angeles Speedway. Arthur had quit driving before Gaston was killed and Louis quit racing cars in 1923. In 1925 Louis tried boat racing and won the Miami Regatta. In 1929, he and Arthur organized the Chevrolet Aircraft Company, to make airplane engines, but the brothers quarreled. Their differences were taken to court and Louis won, but the company failed. Louis went back to work for Chevrolet in 1934, then retired due to a lingering illness in 1938, collecting a small G.M. pension until his death on June 6, 1941. During World War II Arthur went to work for Higgins, who was making plywood boats in New Orleans, as a master mechanic, and hanged himself in 1946 at the age of 61. An inconspicuous gray granite marker, underfoot in Holy Cross cemetery, Indianapolis, constitutes the sole memorial to one of the truly greats in automotive history, Louis Chevrolet, engineer, inventor, designer, builder and sportsman, pioneer of automotive progress.   99

A small marker identifies Louis Chevrolet's grave in an Indianapolis cemetery.

HAROLD WARP
PIONEER VILLAGE FOUNDATION
Minden, Neb. 68959

Key dates in the history of Chevrolet:
1911 - Chevrolet Motor Co. formed.
1914 - Chevrolet's "bowtie" first appears.
1914 - Chevrolet features valve-in-head engine.
1918 - First Chevrolet truck sold.
1918 - Chevrolet joins General Motors Corp.
1918 - Chevrolet offers first radio option in low-priced field.
1927 - Chevrolet outsells Ford.
1929 - Chevrolet's first six-cylinder engine.
1934 - Chevrolet introduces front suspension.
1935 - Carryall Suburban is industry's first all-steel station wagon.
1942 - Chevrolet car production ceases Jan. 30 for World War II.
1945 - Chevrolet car production resumes Oct. 3.
1948 - New postwar pickup design introduced.
1949 - New postwar passenger car introduced.
1950 - Powerglide is first automatic transmission in low-priced field.

In 1927 folks preferred Chevrolet's "stick-shift" to Ford's "high-low" planetary clutch, forcing Ford's Model T to shut down and retool for the Model A.

1953 - Corvette features first fiberglass body.
1955 - Small-block Chevy V-8 introduced.
1957 - RamJet Fuel injection introduced on Chevrolet and Corvette.
1958 - Impala introduced.
1959 - First El Camino pickup.
1960 - Rear-engine Corvair introduced.
1961 - Compact Corvan and Greenbrier passenger van introduced.
1962 - Chevy II announced.
1963 - First Corvette Sting Ray.
1964 - Chevelle announced.
1965 - First Chevrolet Caprice.
1967 - Camaro introduced.
1967 - Camaro paces Indianapolis 500.
1970 - Monte Carlo introduced.
1971 - Vega subcompact introduced.   100

HAROLD WARP
PIONEER VILLAGE
Minden, Neb. 68959 FOUNDATION ®

Powell Crosley built a serviceable and economical car, cheaply, but people preferred to pay more for style.

You could hardly see the Crosley when we all got out and stood in front of it.

1150 MILES FOR $9.08

Crosley - 1939-1952 – The Crosley was built in Cincinnati, Ohio by Powell Crosley, Jr. who made a fortune selling early day radios and refrigerators. Thinking America needed a small car with good mileage, he introduced the 4 passenger, cloth top Crosley at the 1939 New York World's Fair. He arranged to have department stores that sold his appliances also sell his cars. Cannonball Baker, a popular race driver at the time, made a cross-country run in a Crosley, 6500 miles, averaging over 50 miles on a gallon of gasoline, to publicize it. About 4000 Crosleys were sold before World War II.

Most of the parts of the Crosley 4-cylinder, air cooled engine were stamped out of sheet metal and during the war Crosley received lucrative government contracts for his inexpensive engines. In 1946, he introduced several models of the Crosley car and sold 5000 that year at $500 to $800. In 1947, he sold 19,000. In 1949, as larger cars became available, Crosley sales dropped to 7300 units, 6800 in 1950, 6600 in 1951 and 2100 in 1952, which was the Crosley car's final year.   101

Charles F. Kettering

This Ohio farm boy probed all his life for the answers.

Charles Franklin Kettering grew up in wonderment on an Ohio farm. "Why," he asked, peering near-sightedly out of his mother's kitchen window, "can I see through a pane of glass?" "What," he asked, "is magnetism? I would like to know how a magnet reaches and pulls a piece of metal to it." Charlie Kettering was not satisfied with merely asking the questions; all his life he probed for the answers with his pliers, his screw driver, his wrench — and his insatiably curious mind. After teaching a country school three years, Charlie Kettering graduated from Ohio State University in 1904 as an engineer and became an inventor, perhaps the most success-ful of his day.

Why, he wondered, wouldn't the same drive he used to electrify the cash register, work to start a car?

In 1910 a woman driving across Detroit's Belle Isle bridge had engine trouble. Byron Carter, maker of an auto called the Cartercar, happened by, stopped to help, and was cranking furiously away when the motor kicked. The backlashing crank broke his jaw; he later died of complications from the injury. Ket-tering, by then set up in his own Dayton Engineer-ing Laboratories Co. (DELCO), heard of the accident, decided that he would try to do some-thing to prevent others like it. Why couldn't he apply the same principle to start an automobile as he used to crank National Cash Registers, electrically, before he set up "Delco"? With a group of young inventors — the kind that seemed to flock about him all his life — he set to work in a barn hayloft, trying, testing, failing, then trying, testing and fail-ing again. It was part of his system: "You cannot start to do a new thing and hit it right the first time."

During all the years he worked for General Motors, he con-tinued to commute from his home in Dayton, Ohio to Det-roit, Mich.

But within eight months, by disregarding all the rules of the day about electric motors and storage batteries, he had developed the self-starter. Cadillac bought it in 1912 and within a year their car sales doubled.

For the next 45 years Charles Kettering kept prob-ing, testing — often failing. But his successes included "KW" battery ignition, electric farmhome lighting, quick-drying paint, chrome metal, ethyl gasoline, a two-cycle Diesel engine for locomotives — and more than 100 others. He always left friends chuckling with his aphorisms: "I object to people running down the future," he liked to say. "I'm going to live all the rest of my life there." His wife once told him that on his tombstone she would like to engrave the words: "I don't know." By the time he died in December, 1958 at 82, he had amassed a fortune estimated at $50 million.　　102

I.W. Packard

People would pay more for the pride of driving a Packard with the squared off classic radiator from 1903 until 1939.

Packard was first with a twelve cylindar car in 1915.

Packard's demise was in 1958.

In 1898 the Packard brothers, J. W. and W. D., bought a Winton and decided to build a better Horseless Carriage themselves. The first Packard, in 1899, had a single cylinder engine under the seat, central chain drive, 3 forward speeds and reverse gearing, with automatic spark advance. In 1903 their improved Model C, single cylinder Packard, costing $3,000 was driven from San Francisco to New York in 61 days by Fetch and Krarup. That same year they introduced a Big Four that sold for $7,500, followed by the Model L, which carried the first distinctive Packard radiator that would become classic and was to continue through 1939. In 1915 Packard offered the world's first 12 cylinder car – a twin 6 with aluminum pistons at $2,600 and this was the only Packard made for the next four years. In 1920 a Single-Six was offered, selling for $2,350, which accounted for most of Packard's sales until 1928. In 1925, when centralized chassis lubrication was offered, 40,000 Packard Sixes were sold. In 1935 Packard made a bid for the low price market with a car at $980, that had hydraulic brakes and independent front wheel suspension. This was in contrast to the then Standard-eight for $2,475, Super-eight at $2,990 and $3,820 for the 12 cylinder Packard. This small model accounted for 24,995 of the 31,889 Packards sold in 1935. 1939 was the last year of the true "Senior" Packards with the characteristic radiator. The body dies were sold to the Soviet Government, resulting in the 1945 Z.I.S. In 1941 the handsome "Clipper" was introduced, made in 6-cylinder and 8-cylinder versions. It was discontinued during World War II. Production was resumed on the Clipper in 1946 but Packard never regained its former position in the industry. In 1954 they merged with Studebaker and in 1958 the Packard name went down in history.　　103

1901 1-CYLINDER
2¾-H. P. MOTORETTE

1902 1-CYLINDER
3½-H. P. MOTORETTE

1903 2-CYLINDER
15-H. P. TOURING CAR

1904 2-CYLINDER
15-H. P. TOURING CAR

1905 4-CYLINDER
24-28-H. P. TOURING CAR

Pierce-Arrow

It really became a prestige car in 1915 when headlights commenced coming out of the fenders, with its revolutionary sleeve valve engine.

The humble beginning of Pierce-Arrow was the Pierce Motorette, powered by a 2¾ H.P. DeDion engine, produced by bicycle and birdcage builder, George N. Pierce, in 1901. In 1903 the characteristic, Arrow trademark appeared for the first time on a 15 H.P., 2-cylinder model. In 1904 the name was changed to Great Arrow and that year a 28 H.P. Pierce Great Arrow won the Glidden tour. By 1908 power was increased to 60 H.P. In 1909 the name "Great" was dropped and the Pierce-Arrow trademark became one to be admired. Production never seemed to catch up with demand, which was the way George Pierce liked it to be and in 1913 the headlights came out of the front fenders for the first time. It was truly a prestige car by 1915, when over 12,000 had been built, and over half of them were still in everyday use. At that time models sold from $5,850 to $7,300, and was then the largest stock car built in the U.S., with 4 forward speeds. In 1923 sales dropped off and a smaller model was introduced for $2,900, with 4 wheel brakes and an L head, 6-cylinder, 70 H.P. engine. In 1928 control passed to Studebaker Corp. and in 1929 a straight 8 engine powered Pierce was introduced at $2,775. This was destined to be their best year, when 9,700 Pierce-Arrows were sold. In 1930 the famous Pierce-Arrow lines were replaced with Studebaker lines. Resulting sales were disappointing, so in 1933 Studebaker sold Pierce-Arrow back to its original owners and they brought out the Silver Arrow, which was the top car of the 1933 World's Fair. The depression of the 1930s was no time for prestige cars, and in 1935 less than 1,000 Pierce-Arrows were produced and by 1938 production ceased entirely. The famous Pierce-Arrow radiator was retained to the last however, which, as the years have gone by, has become quite an attraction for old car buffs with unlimited funds. 104

HAROLD WARP
PIONEER VILLAGE
Minden, Neb. 68959 FOUNDATION

E.L. Cord

He named "American Airways" in keeping with his control of "American Steamship Lines".

The 1937 "Coffin Nosed Cord" was quite an inovation, with its headlights folding out of fenders and front wheel drive.

He made and sold Trimotor Stinsons for $28,000 and started his own airlines with them during the Depression of the 30s.

In 1925, E.L. Cord, a 30-year-old Chicago Auburn auto salesman, took over the Auburn Auto Company in Auburn, Indiana and introduced the L-29 Cord in 1929 that had front wheel drive. He bought out Eddy Stinson's airplane factory at Northport, Michigan that same year and moved it to Wayne, Michigan in 1930 (now Willow Run Airport). Shortly after Roosevelt closed every bank in the U.S., when elected President in 1932, Erret Cord started American Airways (named after his American Steamship Lines), with 20 fabric covered Trimotor Stinson he built during the Depression, powered by Lycoming radial engines that he had Mr. Woolsey design. He also sold his Trimotor Stinsons to other airlines for $28,000 each. Eddy Rickenbacker started hourly air service between New York and Washington with Cord's Stinson Trimotors and called it General Aviation Corp. With the financial help of General Motors and Lawrence Rockefeller, Rickenbacker later renamed it Eastern Airlines and under his guidance it became the most successful airline for the next 30 years. The depression didn't seem to bother E.L. Cord until in 1937 his two sons were threatened with kidnapping and he started having troubles with the SEC. This caused him to sell all his holdings including auto and aviation interests, a ship building concern as well as other holdings, and moved to England. Some years later he moved back to Nevada, became its state senator in 1950 and died in 1974.   105

HAROLD WARP
PIONEER VILLAGE
Minden, Neb. 68959   FOUNDATION

Henry Kaiser, who made his money in cement, also made a good car, but couldn't compete with the big car makers.

The Kaiser-Frazer Corp. came into being in 1946 when ship-builder, Henry J. Kaiser, and Joseph Frazer of Graham-Paige teamed up to take over the vast Willow Run plant near Detroit, where Henry Ford had been making B-24 bombers. Howard Darrin was hired to design a low priced "Kaiser" and a more expensive "Frazer". Their first car was a "Kaiser Special" with a 6-cylinder 100 BHP Continental engine. In 1949 horsepower was stepped up to 110 and that year the "Vagabond" was introduced. In 1951 the small, cheap "Henry J" was first offered, as was "Allstate" made for Sears

The Frazer was a classy car.

Kaiser also had his hand in making Jeeps.

from 1951 to 1954. They made good cars with a good engine, but they couldn't seem to be able to break into the market as they had hoped to. They lost millions of dollars every year and finally, in 1952, discontinued offering the "Frazer". They then offered the former Frazer as the top car in the Kaiser line, naming it the "Manhattan" at $2,094. In May 1952 they also laid off 3,000 workers permanently at Willow Run. Kaiser merged with Willys in 1953 and that year offered the "Dragon" for $3,628 with radio, air conditioning and automatic transmission. In 1954 the "Manhattan" sedan was made 18 feet long, the Continental engine was stepped up to 140 BHP by addition of a McCullough clutch-controlled supercharger, but this didn't seem to boost sales. Kaiser finally quit fighting Ford, General Motors, Chrysler and American Motors in 1955 in the U.S. and all dies were shipped off to Argentina. In 1967 Renault of Britain purchased the Argentine Kaiser firm, which included the Argentine Jeep, formerly made by Willys.   106

HAROLD WARP
PIONEER VILLAGE
Minden, Neb. 68959 FOUNDATION

In 1953 Chevrolet introduced the Model 2934 Corvette to compete with European sports cars coming into the U.S. after World War II. This was the first production car ever to use a fiberglass body. With a low profile, it had 6-cylinders in line and 3 side-draft carburetors. Priced at $3,513, it was offered in white only. 315 Corvettes were built in 1953. In 1954, a demountable figerglass top was offered for $300 additional. The car weighed 2,800 pounds and 3,000 were built that year. In 1957 the Corvette was made more exotic, with a 283 cubic inch engine that had 4 barrel carburetion, the "hottest" car on the road. It sold for $3,465 and 6,246 Corvettes were made that year. In 1962 a still more extreme "tear-drop" design was offered in Model 0867 and 14,500 were produced at $4,038. By 1965 production reached 23,600. That year the "Sting-Ray" was introduced and in 1967 the "Shark" Corvette came out, with a twin bubble acrylic top and outside exhaust pipes.   107

The Corvette was introduced in 1953 to keep the fancy foreign cars out.

On October 22, 1954 Ford brought out the first Thunderbird, for the young at heart who wanted something different. Its large engine and small body made it competitive with such exotic foreign cars as the Ferrari, and of course, Chevrolet's Corvette. It carried only two people, had a removable hardtop, and weighed 2,980 pounds. 16,155 Thunderbirds had been made by 12-31-55, priced at $2,944. In 1956 the Thunderbird's power was increased to 255 horses and the spare tire was mounted outside in the rear. 15,631 were made in 1956, priced at $3,155. In 1957 the rear section was larger, with more storage space and a tire in the trunk, priced at $3,400. That year 21,380 were made. In 1958 a beautiful 5-passenger prestige convertible Thunderbird was introduced for $4,000, as well as a 2-door hardtop for $3,700. The hardtops outsold the convertibles 35,758 to 2,134. In 1967 the first 4-door T-Bird was introduced, priced at $4,825 and that year the convertible T-Bird was discontinued. Production had increased to 92,465 in 1967. 108

The T-Bird, made for the "young at heart" was an immediate success in 1955.

HAROLD WARP
PIONEER VILLAGE FOUNDATION
Minden, Neb. 68959

Carl Wickland's Hupmobile, driving miners to work, grew up to be Greyhound Bus Lines.

One morning in 1914 a young Swede named Carl Wickman drove a Hupmobile up in front of a saloon in Hibbing, Minnesota, and a bunch of miners piled into the sedan. A miner himself, at 15 cents a head, Wickman drove his passengers four miles to the fire house in Alice, Minnesota, in the heart of the Mesabi iron ore range and the men went to work. Before long Wickman had a co-driver and partner in Andrew Anderson, who was a blacksmith. They called their line Mesabi Transportation Company and soon had another car and a route running 90 miles daily to Duluth. Greyhound Corporation evolved in 1930 from the merger of Wickman's company and another owned by Orville Caesar of Superior, Wisconsin. They bought "Greyhound" buses and chose the running dog as their trademark. From this eventually came the Greyhound bus lines that by 1964 had 5,000 buses and 100,000 miles of routes, with 40,000 employees.

Gleaned from 11-29-64 Chicago Tribune. 109

By 1972 world sales of the Volkswagon Beetle (Model 1200) had exceeded the 15 million Model T Fords produced.

For many years the "Volkswagon", first made in West Germany in 1946 and introduced in America in 1950, was the largest selling foreign car in the U.S. In 1970, there were 569,696 Volkswagons (commonly called "Bugs") sold in the U.S. costing approximately $1,500.00. Only Ford, Chevrolet and Plymouth outsold them in the United States that year. 110

HAROLD WARP **PIONEER VILLAGE** *FOUNDATION*
Minden, Neb. 68959

When Toyota's first attempt to crash the U.S. market bombed in 1961, "Nissan" took no chances with their name, so they introduced the Nissan in 1964 as "Datsun" in the U.S. In 1974 they dropped Datsun in favor of Nissan with a huge U.S. advertising campaign.

Datsun-Nissan: When Japan's Toyota entered the American market in 1961 it "bombed" and did not come back in the American market again until 1964 much improved by American engineers sent to Japan. Nissan, seeing Toyota's failure, didn't want to jeopardise the Japanese Nissan name, in case it flopped in America, so they named it "Datsun", priced at $1,616. It did not sell well until American engineers, sent to Japan by the United States, improved the Datsun to where it commenced competing with American cars in 1964. Twenty years later, Nissan spent huge sums in advertising, to drop the name "Datsun" in the U.S., renaming it "Nissan" which was still being sold in Japan. 111

HAROLD WARP **PIONEER VILLAGE** *FOUNDATION*
Minden, Neb. 68959

Carl Fisher wasn't interested in financing Fred Avery's Prest-O-Lite until he saw it still burning in his garage several days later, when Fred came back to get it.

One day in 1904 Fred Avery approached a young race driver, auto salesman and former bicycle repairman by the name of Carl Fisher in Indianapolis, Indiana, with the idea of compressing gas into a container to mount on the running board of a car to replace carbide lights. Mr. Avery's tank of compressed gas would eliminate the mess of pouring water and lumps of carbide into a copper can mounted on the running board and blending them painstakingly together on the road to produce light, so as to be able to see the wagon ruts at night. Carl Fisher was not interested. The man set the tank in the corner of Fisher's garage, still lit. Several days later Carl Fisher noticed the blue flame was still burning on top of the tank when Avery came back to get it, so Fisher mentioned this to a friend, Jim Allison. The three men formed a

Carl Fisher laid out the Lincoln highway to the west coast and Dixie highway to Miami, to get people to drive these highways at night with his Prest-O-Lite in the days before electric car lights.

partnership to start putting gas into containers under pressure to sell to motorists. Several workers were killed while trying to fill the running board "Prest-O-Lite" tanks with gas. Occasionally a tank would let go for no apparent reason while the gas was being pumped in, creating a terrific explosion. Three years later the problem was finally solved by packing the containers with asbestos to absorb the shock of the incoming gas, and Carl Fisher and his partners were on their way to undreamed of wealth. Fisher and Allison sold their interest in Prest-O-Lite in 1913 for $9,000,000, to the Union Carbide & Carbon Company, that later discovered "Prestone" antifreeze and "Vinylite" plastic as residues.

Carl invested his money in a 500 mile race track that he called "The Indianapolis Speedway" and in a bridge and a swamp near Miami, Florida that he named Collins Road and Miami Beach, while Jim Allison invested his share of the profits in racing cars and "Allison Motors". We do not know what became of Fred Avery, who originally brought the compressed gas idea over from France. While Carl Fisher's wife was in Paris during his development of Miami Beech, he wired her $86,000 one day for some lots he had sold. She proceeded to spend it all in one afternoon in one jewelry store. He went broke in the crash of 1929 while developing Montauk Point on Long Island and died a lonely man, in a Miami Beach rooming house, in his late sixties on July 15, 1939.   112

Carl Fisher of Indianapolis, Indiana laid out the Lincoln and Dixie Highways from coast to coast and border to border (1913-1915) to sell his Prestolite (to see to drive a car at night) and to sell his white Indiana limestone that he quarried (to see the road to drive a car at night). Instead, electric lights, concrete and asphalt were purchased.   113

Tourists followed the signs on fence posts and telephone posts.

On the beach, east of Miami, Mr. Collins built a bon fire in 1913 and men cut a swath through the mangroves to it, from Miami to Miami Beach, that became Collins Road.

"Cut her wide, boys" were Carl Fisher's orders as Lincoln Road, now Miami Beach's well-known fashion shopping avenue, was hacked from dense mangrove forests in 1913. Carl Fisher laid out the partially developed Miami Beach, Florida as the southern terminus of his Dixie Highway to help heal the wounds of the North and the South, after he had laid out the Lincoln Highway coast to coast, across the northern states.   114

First concrete mile, a single lane, built in 1909 in Wayne County, Michigan.

Contrary to popular belief, the horseless carriage's arch rival – the horse – led the way for America's roads. At Bellefontaine, Ohio in 1892, city officials laid the first 10 ft. strips of concrete at hitching rails to replace macadam that was torn up by pawing horses. In 1893 the streets around the courthouse square were paved with concrete. In 1909 the first concrete mile was built, a single lane in Wayne County, Michigan, under the supervision of Edward N. Hines. Early road building equipment including chisel plows, scrapers, fresnos, wagons, graders and steam rollers are among the 50,000 historical items that are on display at the Harold Warp Pioneer Village Foundation in south central Nebraska.   115

First transcontinental highways built by local people.

This country's first transcontinental highways were built and maintained by local merchants and farmers. Each six square mile township built their portion of the highway. In 1917, Harold Warp (author of this book) when 14 years of age, operated a 2-horse team and a "Fresno" to help build the highway across May Township in Kearney County, Nebraska. He was paid 50¢ per day by the owner of the team of horses. W.A. Johnson, who received $2.00 per day for man and horses. Each township built their portion of the highway.   116

How U.S. Highway 6 Evolved:

1910 - Between Omaha, Lincoln and Denver (OLD) white band on three poles per mile – done by volunteer workers in each county, preferably a band sixteen inches wide, but most posts just had a dash of white on them.

1913 - Farmers in each county, living along the route, donated work and teams for grading. Each road district through which the O-L-D passed furnished culverts and a grader.

1919 - A fourteen inch white band and three inch black band, top and bottom, done by field men. Paid by road enthusiasts in each town between Omaha and Denver.

1925 - First gravel spread on O-L-D.

1926 - Highway extended to Detroit and O-L-D changed to D-L-D. For the first time, letters D-L-D were stenciled vertically on center (white) band.

First stop signs erected in 1928.

1928 - First stop signs erected by State Road Department. Graveling completed across the state of Nebraska, done mostly by farmers as a government relief project, as the collapse of grain prices made farming unprofitable.

First transcontinental road signs in 1935.

1935 - Highway extended coast to coast and D-L-D changed to U.S. No. 6. Black top paving started. Signs erected, first wood, later metal "U.S. 6". (Cape Cod to Los Angeles)

1950 - Black top completed across Nebraska on U.S. 6.

1958 - Nebraska's portion of a 40,000 mile Interstate Highway system was commenced. The U.S. Government furnished 90% of the cost of this road, the State furnished the remaining 10% as well as the right of way. The U.S. Department of Engineers recommended where the road should be built. Interstate 80 was completed across Nebraska in 1967.

117

HAROLD WARP
PIONEER VILLAGE FOUNDATION
Minden, Neb. 68959

500 Fascinating Facts

Nebraska Auto & Gas Taxes

1905 - The first automobile registration fee of $1.00 per car was levied.

1911 - Automobile registration fees raised to $2.00 per year.

1925 - The first gasoline tax of two cents a gallon was levied.

1926 - State Highway maintenance system started.

1929 - Gasoline tax increased to four cents a gallon.

1935 - Gasoline tax was increased to five cents a gallon.

1949 - Legislature increased tax to six cents per gallon.   118

Minden, Neb. 68959

There is no original 1903 "Wright Brothers" "Kitty Hawk" flying machine. It cracked up in their last flight attempt that December day in 1903. They had proved it would fly, left its broken parts at Kill Devil Hill, and went home to build an improved model with more horsepower, that they flew off of Mr. Huffman's cow pasture at Dayton, Ohio. In 1904 they made 105 flights off of Huffman's pasture with their improved "Flyer". They never returned to Kill Devil Hill, four miles south of Kittyhawk, North Carolina. In 1914, after Wilbur's death, Orville was persuaded to rebuild a copy of their original flying machine. He more or less built the replica from memory, resurrecting a few broken pieces at Kill Devil Hill from their flights there eleven years earlier.   119

Wright brothers' "Kitty Hawk" flying machine at Smithsonian not original. Made from memory in 1914 by Orville Wright.

Minden, Neb. 68959

An exact replica of the Wright Brothers "Kitty Hawk" at the Smithsonian was built under the direction of H.P. Boen in Kobe, Japan in 1962 using blueprints of Orville Wright's replica. It was delivered to Harold Warp's Pioneer Village in Minden, Nebraska in 1964 and placed on display there in 1965. According to aerodynamics, as they are known today, the Wright Brothers' 1903 flying machine should have been unable to fly.   120

By today's standards, Wright brothers' "Kitty Hawk" should be unable to fly.

45 years after Wright brothers' first flight, Kitty Hawk brought back from England, 11 months after Orville Wright died.

In 1928 Orville Wright lent their rebuilt Kitty Hawk to London, England's Science Museum because the Smithsonian Institute in Washington, D.C. did not acknowledge the Wright Brothers as being the first to fly. Furthermore, Orville considered the building he had it stored in all those years since rebuilt in 1914, to be a firetrap. On October 8, 1942, C.G. Abbot, then director of Smithsonian Institute, withdrew the mis-statements they had made about the Wright Brothers and offered full apology. This apology came after Orville Wright had known for 28 years that Glenn Curtiss received $2,000 from the Smithsonian Institute in 1914 to modify the Langley flying machine, using aerodynamics originally discovered by the Wrights, and never possessed by Langley, to make the Langley flyable. Orville Wright subsequently notified the Science Museum of South Kensington, London, England, that he wished to have their reconstructed "Kitty Hawk" flying machine returned to the United States. Toward the end of 1948 it was brought back and hung overhead at the Smithsonian with much formal ceremony on December 17, just 45 years after the Wright Brothers' first flight and just 11 months after Orville Wright had died on January 30, 1948.   121

It was only by chance that the United States kept aviation leadership. France paid the Wright Brothers 25,000 francs ($5,000) toward an option to buy their newly granted flying machine patents for 1,000,000 francs ($200,000) on May 22, 1906. But because the brothers were secretive, unassuming men, France considered them "fakers" and forfeited the $5,000. The brothers used the $5,000 for further flying machine development. They had accepted France's offer when the United States government did not seem interested in purchasing any Wright Brothers flying machines after their patents had been granted.   122

France forfeited $5,000 down payment for purchase of Wright brothers' flying machine patents when told they were "fakers".

Wright brothers' "Kitty Hawk" engine manifold made from old tomato can.

Don't throw away your old tomato can. The engine of the first Wright Bros. plane – the Kittyhawk – was built in 1903 by the brothers themselves. The metal cylinder on top of the intake manifold was a carburetor made from an old tomato can. Some 50 engines and 20 planes trace the evolution of aviation at the Harold Warp Pioneer Village at Minden, Nebraska's #1 attraction. 123

Orville once said, "Learning the secret of flight from a bird was a good deal like learning the secret of magic from a magician. After you once know the trick and know what to look for, you see things that you did not notice when you did not know exactly what to look for." 124

"Secrets of flight — was like learning secrets of a magician," said Orville Wright, adding "we didn't think it would ever be possible to fly or make landings at night."

In later years, when Orville Wright was asked when in his lifetime he got his biggest "kick" out of inventing free flight he replied, "while lying in bed, before I had ever been in the air at all – thinking how exciting it would be to fly." He also stated, "When we first flew we were not thinking of any practical uses at all. We didn't suppose it would ever be possible to fly or make landings at night." 125

Bishop Milton Wright (Wright brothers' father) once stated "Only angels fly, men will never fly, God has so ordained it."

In 1877 Bishop Milton Wright listened to a sermon by a young preacher who predicted that one day man would be able to fly. Bishop Wright, much disturbed, after Brother Horner's sermon, took occasion to correct the young man's thinking. "You spoke," he said, "of expecting to see men flying overhead in machines yet to be invented. That, Brother Horner, is a sacreligious error, for only angels fly. Men will never fly; God has so ordained it." The Bishop who made that statement was the father of Orville and Wilbur Wright, who invented the airplane. 126

For 207 minutes work, Charles K. Hamilton earned $10,000 dollars. How? By flying the first airmail from New York to Philadelphia and back, on June 13, 1910. This historic plane, as well as 19 others, can be seen at the Harold Warp Pioneer Village at Minden in south central Nebraska.   127

Charles K. Hamilton, 1881-1914.

First airmail pilot.

Our first flying machines were not built by financiers who risked their fortunes, but by boys in barns and backyards who risked their lives. The Wright Brothers ran a bicycle repair shop. Glenn Martin built his first plane in 1909 in a Santa Anna, California church. Bill Boeing built his first flying boat in an abandoned Seattle boat yard in 1916. Donald Douglas' dream took shape in back of a Santa Monica, California barber shop in 1920. Matty Laird's first plane took wing in 1913 at 21st and Cicero, Chicago – what was then farmland. Clyde Cessna built his monoplane in an Enid, Oklahoma garage in 1910. The first airplane passenger Charles W. Furnas, flew with Wilbur Wright in 1908.   128

Boys built first flying machines in barns, sheds, even a church.

Ice Scale and Tachometer were early day flight instruments. Before taking off with an early day flying machine an ice scale was tied to the tail and staked down. A tachometer was placed on the propellor hub. By reading these two instruments the pilot could determine whether the engine was turning up properly and he could also tell if there was enough "lift" in the air to enable him to take off. The "dig" of the "prop" would register in pounds of pull on the ice scale. "Flying Machines" were not called "Aeroplanes" until 1917.   129

Flying machines not called Aeroplanes until 1917.

The American Curtiss flying boat NC-4 made the first Atlantic crossing in 1919. The pioneer flight was carried out in stages from Jamaica Bay over the Azores to Lisbon's harbor.   130

First flight across Atlantic in 1919.

When war was declared on April 6, 1917 the U.S. Signal Corps did not own a combat "Flying Machine" as they were then called. Of the thirteen JN-4D (Jennies) the Signal Corps had purchased previously, seven had crashed and six had been destroyed in the Mexican War. During 1917 and 1918 the U.S. Government took delivery of 4,950 of JN-4 Curtiss airplanes, powered by OX-5 motors. Their V-8 cylinders developed 90 horsepower and flew 60 miles per hour, with a top speed of 70. Gross flyable weight was 1,900 pounds. In 1917 this was the highest powered U.S. war plane and the first flying machine to be built in quantities for the U.S. Government. After World War I, these "Jennies" were sold to "Barn Stormers" for as little as $550. (The writer among them, as Secretary of Chicago Flying Club at Thatcher and Irving Park Road, Chicago) 131

When World War I was declared, the U.S. owned no combat flying machines.

Flat spins were deadly. The Swallow Biplane, the first airplane to be introduced commercially in 1920, had a bad habit of getting into an uncontrollable flat spin, if allowed to spin too long on maneuvers, which had resulted in several deaths. Harold Warp had a Swallow that cost $2750.00 in 1927, that he used for throwing samples of his Flex-O-Glass over towns, then landing nearby and offering a dealer and his family a ride if he would put in Flex-O-Glass. When Mr. Warp purchased the Swallow he had the seats built so that they would accommodate the newly developed Irwin parachutes. One Sunday he took the Swallow up to film moving pictures of a spin. Mr. Warp was in the front seat of the Swallow taking pictures while a fellow pilot was in the back seat flying the airplane. When Mr. Warp had taken his pictures he advised the pilot to pull out of the spin. The pilot (Gus Linquist) replied, "I can't." After spinning a couple of rounds in a flat spin, directly over a cemetery, they decided to jump out, using the parachutes. As they stood up to jump, the ship righted itself and they didn't have to use their parachutes. Thus it was discovered that to kill a flat spin, the pilot should stand up, which would disrupt the air currents that caused it. 132

Flat spins could be broken by standing up in cockpit.

Early flying machines had tail-skids and wing-skids for brakes.

For the first 25 years after the Wright Brothers first flew in 1903, flying machines had large landing wheels to allow for landing on rough terrain. All early flying machines had tail skids to dig into the sod as well as skids on the outer end of the lower wings of biplanes to act as a skid when it became necessary to break a ground loop when landing in a short field, to avoid hitting an obstacle ahead. 133

Straight ahead vision was impossible in take-offs and landings.

When open cockpits first appeared on flying machines in the 'teens, in taking off or landing it was necessary to stick one's head out of one side of the cockpit or the other for two reasons: to feel the speed of the wind on the pilot's face and see where the airplane was headed. 134

Farm windmills told wind direction, because "forced landings" were common.

Thousands of Curtiss OX-5 motors were built during World War I, that the U.S. Government sold later to airplane manufacturers for $250 or less. For that reason nearly all airplanes built in the 1920s had 90 H.P., 8 cylinder OX-5 engines. The "OX-5" had a tendency to stop abruptly under certain atmospheric conditions; when a ball of ice would form in the bottom of the air intake and get sucked into the fuel supply tube, or the ignition points on the magneto would suddenly stick together, causing an abrupt landing. Pilots seldom flew cross-country over 1500 feet above the ground, in order to keep a suitable landing field in sight at all times and to be able to see the direction of the wind from observing waves in grain fields or the direction of the fan on windmills, as it was always necessary to land into the wind. 135

Bendix brakes became necessary with cement airport runways.

When airports and cement runways began to appear in the 1930s, it became necessary to replace the tail skid on the airplane with a tail wheel, as the cement runway would grind up the tail skid as it slid over the hard surface. This also necessitated brakes. Bendix introduced the first airplane wheel brakes in 1930. 136

Matty Laird was first commercial airplane builder, "Swallow" 1919.

"Swallow" Biplane: When Matty Laird designed the very first commercial airplane in a Wichita, Kansas shed, hotel man Bill Lassen said, when they first flew it: "There she goes, boys, just like a Swallow." E.M. "Matty" Laird built 40 Swallows at Wichita, Kansas between 1919 and 1923; that was more than all other planes combined. Swallows were used to start the United Airlines. One of the first (NC4809) hangs overhead at the Harold Warp Pioneer Village, Minden, Nebraska among 20 historic flying machines.   137

HAROLD WARP
PIONEER VILLAGE
Minden, Neb. 68959 FOUNDATION

Timberman William Edward Boeing, a venturesome millionaire became interested in aviation when he purchased a pontoon airplane in 1915 from Glenn L. Martin to fish remote lakes and streams of British Columbia. The plane was built too light to satisfy Boeing, so he decided to build his own plane. The first factory was an old Seattle boatyard. There Boeing first built a 3,200 pound, 125 horsepower, 78 mile per hour wood and linen seaplane. In the years thereafter, Boeing made a land-based biplane that was the U.S.'s first efficient mail carrier; it helped him to win the profitable San Francisco-Chicago route. Boeing's Monomail 200 in 1930 was the first plane with retractable landing gear; his 1933 ten passenger Boeing 247 was the U.S.'s first twin engine commercial transport plane, and the Boeing Stratoliner in 1938 was the first transport with a pressurized cabin. As early as 1934 Boeing had drawn up plans for a four-engined bomber; the U.S. War Department turned it down as being too visionary. Bill Boeing thereupon spent $275,000 of his own money to build the plane. During World War II, it became the famed B-17 Flying Fortress.

Bill Boeing's first seaplane.

William E. Boeing
1882-1956

Bill Boeing's plans for a four engine bomber was "too visionary" for the U.S. government, so he built it hiimself (at a cost of $275,000). It became the famous "B-17 Flying Fortress" in World War II.

Bill Boeing became angered by a 1934 U.S. Government decision that forced him to split his aircraft manufacturing company and his newly thriving airmail and passenger service. He, therefore, let go of the carrier that became United Air Lines, the U.S.'s largest domestic trunk line. He became so embittered that he sold out all his Boeing Company holdings and never after 1935 played an active part in running his own company. He died in 1956 at the age of 74.   138

500 Fascinating Facts

United Airlines' first flight, 4/6/26.

"Speed" Holman rejuvenated Northwest Airlines in 1928, with a Laird.

Eddy Stinson's fabric covered monoplanes started American, Delta and Eastern Airlines.

Eddie Rickenbacker renamed the New York-Washington run Eastern Airlines in 1934.

Ercoupe, purchased new in 1941, still using Warp's original log books 40 years later, when repurchased.

Airlines that started operations with 1926 Laird Swallows:

United Airlines – April 6, 1926 – (Varney - 2 Swallows), Elko, Nevada to Pasco, Washington.

Northwest Airlines – June 7, 1926 – (Dickinson - 2 Swallows), Minneapolis to Chicago. Partridge crashed to his death on first flight   139

Airlines that started operations with Stinsons:

Wien Alaska Airlines – 1926 – (Noel & Ralph Wien bought Explorer Sir Hubert Wilkins' Stinson and started Wien Alaska in 1926.)

Northwest (Reorganized) – October 1, 1927 – Pilots: Dave Behncke, Chester Jacobson, C.W. (Speed) Holman. 3 Stinson Detroiters, Chicago to Milwaukee

Braniff Airlines – 1927 – (Tom & Paul Braniff) Stinson Detroiter, Oklahoma City to Tulsa

Delta Airlines – 1934 – (C.E. Woolman) Used Stinsons, Charleston, S.C. to Dallas, Texas

American Airlines – 1932 – (E.L. Cord's Century Airlines and Century Pacific) Stinson Tri-Motors

Eastern Airlines – September, 1930 – Ludington's New York, Philadelphia, Washington Route (E.L. Cord's Stinson Tri-Motors every hour, absorbed by Eastern February 1933.) *From "Airways" by Smith*   140

Ercoupe Airplane #NC37100, purchased new by Harold Warp in 1941, was flown by him for the next five years. He then sold it. He bought it back 40 years later, still in flying condition in 1981, to hang in his Pioneer Village at Minden, Nebraska. Surprisingly his original airframe and engine log books were still being used 40 years later (to record hours flown and by whom). These log books, still in the Ercoupe, show that Mr. Warp flew this Ercoupe more hours in the five years he had it than it was flown in the next 35 years.   141

Oldest U.S. jet aircraft at Pioneer Village.

The oldest jet aircraft in the United States is on display at the Harold Warp Pioneer Village at Minden in south central Nebraska. This P-59 was the second jet built by the Bell Aircraft Co. in 1942. The first jet was flight tested in California where it crashed. The second jet was sent to Purdue University in Lafayette, Indiana for instrument testing. It was obtained from the U.S. Government after World War II by Harold Warp to hang at his Pioneer Village at Minden, Nebraska. 142

The world's first four engine plane was designed in 1912 by Igor Sikorsky and built in Russia before he migrated to the U.S. 143

Sikorsky and his first helicopter.

Howard Hughes flew around the world in three days, 19 hours and eight minutes with a crew of four. Wiley Post, in a Lockheed Vega in 1931, again in 1933, flew alone around the world in seven days and 18 hours. Amelia Earhart, flying a Lockheed Electra in July 1937, disappeared in the Pacific. 144

Lockheed monoplanes made record flights.

Zeppelin – The cigar-shaped airship that could be steered and propelled, and that at one time seemed to have a big future in aviation, is named after Count Ferdinand von Zeppelin, the German who invented its rigid frame. 145

Mr. Zeppelin's airship disappeared in a flaming inferno over Atlantic City in 1931.

Rising smoke from an open fire that carried bits of paper into the air sparked the idea of heated air balloons for Joseph Montgolfier in 1783. He and his brother tested a 35 foot (diameter) balloon by filling it with hot air. When cast off the balloon rose to 6000 feet and settled down to earth a mile away. An early balloon basket, together with 20 historic early flying machines, can be seen at the Harold Warp Pioneer Village, Minden, Nebraska. 146

A bon fire sparked Montgolfier's first baloon in 1783.

First solo flight by American woman 1910.

Blanche Stuart Scott was the first American woman to make a public flight. She was a student of aviation pioneer Glenn Curtiss, and made her solo flight October 23, 1910, at the Driving Park, Fort Wayne, Ind. She used an Ely aircraft and reached an altitude of 12 feet.   147

First 'round the world flight, U.S. Army pilots 1924.

The first round the world flight was made in 1924 by six U.S. Army pilots in three open cockpit biplanes. They traveled 26,103 miles in 57 flights, from Seattle to Seattle, in a little less than six months.

The first round the world flight by one man was in 1933, when Wiley Post, (who had only one eye) flew it in seven days, 18 hours, alone.   148

First solo 'round the world flight, Wiley Post, 1933.

From Aerospace Historian, Spring 1966 – After the first World War, at McCook Field, Dayton, Ohio, I was assigned as pilot to make motion pictures of aircraft in flight. One of my first missions was to fly Sergeant Louis Hagenmeyer with his high-speed (180 frames per second) Bell and Howell camera over the flying field and make slow-motion pictures of a live parachute jump to show the actuation of the chute. During this period pilots did not wear parachutes and the Air Service had set a high priority on developing one. An English parachute inventor and his daughter had arrived at the field to demonstrate their "Guardian Angel" parachute. It was planned that the inventor would jump out of a DH4 airplane at 4,000 feet over McCook Field, and that I would fly in another DH4 and place Hagenmeyer in a position to follow the opening of the chute all the way down to the landing. The Englishman jumped, and in doing so, he slipped and his parachute harness was ripped off his body when it caught on a control projection on the side of the airplane. His daughter watched her father fall to his death but she was so intent on proving the trustworthiness of the parachute that within a couple of hours she donned the chute and made a successful demonstration jump. – George W. Goddard, Brig. Gen'l. U.S.A.F. (Ret.)   149

Inventor of parachute killed in first demonstration.

Wind on the face was the air speed indicator before cabin planes sported air speed guages.

Closed cabin airplanes did not appear until an air speed indicator was invented that could be mounted on the dash, in the mid-twenties. Previously the pilot had to feel the speed of the wind on his face to determine speed. Chas. Lindbergh had the Spirit of St. Louis built in 1928 so he could stick his head out of the window.   150

HAROLD WARP
PIONEER VILLAGE FOUNDATION
Minden, Neb. 68959

Yale law student Cameron B. Waterman's first crude efforts at propelling a boat was an air-cooled bicycle motor that he mounted on the stern of his fishing craft. This worked well in principle but in 1905 tests on the Detroit River proved that the chain could be easily knocked off the lower sprocket. Then Waterman and his friend George Thrall, the only one who didn't laugh at Waterman's idea, adopted a very satisfactory driveshaft and bevel gear arrangement. Waterman, in 1905, coined the term "out board motor" but he was unable to copyright it because of its generic derivation. In his patent No. 851,839, The Waterman Porto was described as a "self-contained motor and propeller". His first model was a two-horsepower, single-cylinder, water-cooled engine weighing 40 pounds. In 1906 Waterman sold his first 25 outboards. Evinrude marketed his first outboard in 1909 and sold out his outboard interests in 1914. Waterman's career in the outboard industry ended in 1917 when he sold his interests to the Arrow Motor and Marine Company of New York, having made some 30,000 Portos. Waterman died in 1956 at the age of 79, a successful Milwaukee lawyer and devoted sportsman. Few realized the part he played in recreational boating.   151

Bicycle motor sparked first (Waterman) outboard.

HAROLD WARP
PIONEER VILLAGE FOUNDATION
Minden, Neb. 68959

Ole Evinrude tested his one-cylinder outboard on Milwaukee's Kinnickinnac River in 1908 and by 1913 he was offered $350,000 for his Evinrude Company by Chris Meyer, which he and his wife, Bess, accepted. They then bought a cruiser and went down the Mississippi River to Florida. Their son, Ralph, who eventually was to head Outboard Marine, Waukegan, Ill., was then one year old. After

Ole Evinrude made outboards practical and economical.

loafing for two years, Ole commenced designing a new light twin to be made mostly of aluminum. He designed a 47 pound twin that was 27 pounds lighter than the single cylinder Evinrude he had sold to Meyer. When Ole went to Meyer in 1920 with his new light twin, he was turned down, so he started building it himself in 1921, taking the name ELTO from the first letters of Evinrude Light Twin Outboard. By 1928 Ole took over the faltering Evinrude Company and joined forces with Briggs and Stratton to form Outboard Marine Corp. In 1935 they also took over the faltering Johnson, with headquarters in Waukegan, Illinois.

Total Outboard Motor Sales:

    1919 — 17,000
    1929 — 59,000
    1932 — 12,000   152

1921 Johnson

The Johnson brothers built airplanes, speed boats and bicycle motors prior to Johnson outboards.

The Johnson Motor Company was organized in December 1921 to build a two-cylinder, 2 H.P., 2,200 R.P.M., 35 lb. "Waterbug" that would swing completely around, to sell for $140. It was an immediate success. That first year the Johnson boys, Lou, Harry and Clarence, sold 3,000 Johnson Waterbugs and in 1923 they sold 7,000. The Johnson boys had built the first monoplane in the United States to be powered by its own motor, also designed by them, at Terre Haute, Indiana in 1912. They also opened an aviation school and built inboard speed boats. In 1917 they started making little 1½ H.P. air cooled engines in South Bend to fasten to bicycles. These Johnson enterprises all petered out in the depression of 1920, before they went to building outboard motors. In 1925 the Johnson boys added a single cylinder 1½ H.P., 27 lb. motor and in 1926 they also added a 6 H.P. model to their line. By 1929 they had graduated to "Sea Horses" up to 32 H.P. and were building a million dollar plant in Waukegan, Illinois, when the '29 Crash came. That year they spent $600,000 in advertising. The Johnson Motor Company was taken over by Ole Evinrude's Outboard Marine Co., in 1935, but was kept as a competitor by Ole's son Ralph.   153

The first steam turbine was tested in a boat by Parsons in 1896. Today all jet airplanes and locomotives are turbine powered.   154

Don Aronow introduced powerboating to the world of Speed. He founded fast-boat companies, made their names household words in boating circles and sold them with the ease of a born entrepreneur — Donzi, Formula, Magnum, Cigarette and Squadron XII. His boats set 25 world speed records and won more than 300 races. The most famous of all his designs was the Cigarette. Aronow's most recent contribution to boating was an even faster craft called Blue Thunder. He got the idea for naming his fledgling Donzi company in a small bar with some boating buddies when a waitress recognized Aronow and greeted him with "Donzi, baby!" Aronow mulled over the name that night; the next day he decided on the name for his new firm. His untimely death the afternoon of Feb. 3, 1987 near his 60th birthday, stunned the boating world. He was fatally shot as he sat in his car in the middle of Northeast 188th Street in Miami in the heart of a powerboat manufacturing empire he had created and ruled for the past quarter-century. He had retired when 30 and went to Florida, after which he decided to build racing boats.   155

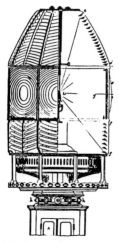

A barroom waitress' greeting "Donzi Baby" sparked the name for Don Aronow's first racer.

"Bullseye" lighthouse lenses were invented in 1828 by Augustin Fresnel, a Frenchman. A curved reflector could increase one candle power by 20,000 times, but this Bullseye, with calculated prisms, each at a different angle, could increase one candle power over 80,000 times. On a clear night one candle power could be seen for over 18 miles. It was rotated by clock works, powered by huge weights that the lighthouse tender had to wind up periodically. In stormy weather the lighthouse tender cleansed these prisms several times a night. The last U.S. civilian lighthouse keeper was Annie Salter of Turkey Point Lighthouse on Chesapeake Bay, who retired in 1947.   156

Lighthouse lenses were intricately designed to increase one candle-power 80,000 times.

Ship's figure heads landed in front of cigar stores.

In the early 1800s few American sailships left port without a carved figurehead at their prows, but by 1840 there was little demand for these decorations on ships. American tobacconists commenced buying these old figureheads in the 1850s – particularly Indians, to "advertise" their shops. Thus Tom Millard, who had been carving ships' figureheads started a shop for the manufacture of wooden cigar store Indians and promoted them so successfully that his company thrived for fifty years. Their gaudily painted decorations had to be renewed so frequently that some artists made a living doing nothing else. There were at one time some 75,000 Cigar Store Indians scattered over the country where cigars were sold. By 1900 they were on their way out, and by 1930 they had gone down in history.   157

Robert Fulton, a landscape and portrait artist, built and sailed the first steam powered launch up the Hudson from New York to Albany, August 11, 1807, completing the trip in 32 hours. He was then 42 and he died at 50, after much legal action defending his patents.   158

Robert Fulton's boat steamed up the Hudson River in 1807.

Crows brought Vikings home when released from their cage on the mast, prior to compasses.

The crows-nest on ancient Viking ships was where crows were kept caged on a platform, high on the mast. The crows would be released for the sailors to follow to land, if lost. Whalers replaced the crows cage with a barrel in which a lookout stood as he scouted for whales in the "Crows-Nest."   159

First casting bait patented in 1889.

Bait casting for fish is purely American. James Clark of Chicago put a reel on a six foot stick of bamboo in 1885, to cast live frogs for bass. James Heddon, a Michigan man, in 1889 patented the first (wooden) bass plug with fish hooks fastened to it.   160

An English druggist, while cleaning his mixing paddle, it burst into flame, sparking the first match.

An English druggist, John Walker, in 1827, had mixed up some antimony sulphide and potassium chloride in his Stockton-on-Tees Pharmacy. As he bent down to scrape his mixing stick on the store floor to clean it, the stick burst into flames. Previously, striking flints together was the most common way to start a fire. He started making wooden matches in 1833, dipping both ends in his concoction. To ignite them, they were drawn quickly through folded sandpaper. He called them "Lucifers". Alonzo D. Phillips brought them to the United States under the fancy name of "Locofocos". 161

A piece of cardboard sparked the first book matches in 1892.

The first book matches were invented in 1892 by Joshua Pussey, a Philadelphia lawyer. He cut the matches out of a piece of cardboard with his office scissors. In 1895 Pussey sold his book match patent to the Diamond Match Company and the first advertising to appear on book matches was a hand lettered ad put out by the Mendelson Opera Co., New York City, in 1896. 162

Coal was considered poisonous in England, while being used by Hopi Indians in America to heat their huts.

Arizona was the scene of the first use of coal in North America. The Hopi Indians as early as A.D. 1000 heated their houses and kivas with coal. In Old England coal was believed to fill the air with poisonous gases. In 1306, the English monarch issued a proclamation declaring anyone who burned coal would be put to death. 163

Col. Drake couldn't keep his oil money. Neither could other inventors.

Col. Edward Drake dug the first oil well 69½ feet deep on Oil Creek, Pennsylvania on August 27, 1859. He made a fortune in oil, but lost it all and died a pauper in 1880. The inventors of the typewriter, chronograph watch, and twine binder also died broke. 164

Kerosene called "skunk oil" when first distilled in 1859.

When kerosene was first distilled from crude oil discovered in 1859, it was referred to as "skunk oil" due to its disagreeable odor. With improved refining the disagreeable odor of kerosene disappeared and for the next fifty years it was called "coal oil". 165

Minden, Neb. 68959

John D. Rockefeller's fortune came from 25,000 standard oil wagons filling 50 gallon barrels with kerosene on farmsteads everywhere. It was then difficult to dispose of the dangerous useless gasoline.

Between 1890 and 1920 John D. Rockefeller's Standard Oil wagons, 25,000 of them, pulled by 67,000 horses and mules, filled 50 gallon barrels at farmsteads everywhere in the U.S.A., with kerosene and later also gasoline. The barrels were located somewhere out in the yard, usually standing in the shade of a tree. These dangerous fuels were never stored indoors. Kerosene and later gasoline stoves usually stood out on the porch. 166

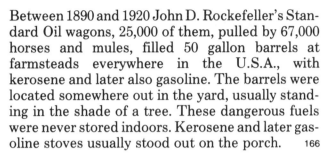

Minden, Neb. 68959

His wife's vase sparked the name for Bob Cheeseborough's "Vaseline".

In the fall of 1859, the same year that Colonel Ed Drake discovered oil at Titusville, Pennsylvania, a young chemist named Robert Cheeseborough, while watching that first well pump oil, noticed a collection of colorless residue collecting on the pump rod at the top of the well. He began experimenting and eventually discovered a way to extract the wax from the crude oil, that he called "Petroleum Jelly." Believing this new product had healing powers, he inflicted burns and wounds on his body that he treated with his soothing balm, that made him feel better. He even swallowed a teaspoon full in the mornings, claiming it improved his health. His wife kept his laboratory supplied with fresh flowers each day. He commenced using the flower vase for his petroleum jelly. She suggested he name it vaseline. (The "line" being the vase suffix for most patent medicines). Robert Cheeseborough died in 1933, age ninety-six, but the Cheeseborough Company kept on making vaseline. 167

Minden, Neb. 68959

Gasoline and Ethylene once worthless by-products.

At the turn of the century gasoline was a worthless byproduct of kerosene, considered very dangerous and difficult to dispose of, just as ethylene gas became a refinery torch a half century later, being burned off at the well site, at the top of a pipe high in the air. (By 1965, however, ethylene gas was in short supply for use in producing plastics.) 168

Butane and Propane burned off at well sight for 69 years.

"L.P. Gas" commonly used for heating in homes, where natural gas is not available, was burned off with a flame at the top of a small pipe, high in the air, at almost every well site for over 70 years. (1859 until 1928) Butane and propane are low pressure (L.P.) gasses that liquify at less than 15 pounds of pressure. Therefore they came out of the oil well as a gas until 1928 when the oil companies started catching and compressing these gasses into portable tanks and commenced selling "LP Gas" at 5¢ per gallon, primarily to farmers, where natural gas was not available. 169

Candle powered fan.

The candle powered fan was a far cry from the multiple speed intake and exhaust fans of today. The kerosene powered fan followed in 1890, water propelled fan in 1900 and battery powered in 1910. 170

Spark ignition prohibited until 1895 when Mr. Otto's engine patent expired, fired by a blow torch.

Nikolaus August Otto, in Germany, patented the first internal combustion engine in 1877, using a blow torch to ignite compressed gases through a tiny hole in the end of the cylinder. When spark ignition was invented, Otto refused to use it on his engine, so spark ignition was not used until Otto's patent ran out in 1895. You can see Otto's very first 1877 internal combustion engine at Harold Warp's Pioneer Village Foundation at Minden in south central Nebraska. 171

Mr. Rudolph Diesel's revolutionary engine would even run on coal dust or molasses, patented in 1892. Adolph Busch, St. Louis, MO, was Mr. Diesel's first U.S. customer in 1896, with which to make Budweiser beer.

In 1893 Rudolph Diesel, a German scientist and inventor, born in Paris in 1858 of Bavarian parentage, described a new form of internal combustion engine which we now know as the Diesel engine. Diesel's first engine was patented in 1892, the inventor claiming to have originated a compression-ignition engine to burn coal dust blown into the engine cylinder by compressed air, although it was further claimed any kind of fuel could be used. The principle of the Diesel engine is to compress air into approximately 1/16th the space it normally takes, which simultaneously generates heat above the flash point of such inexpensive fuels as powered coal, crude oil, fish oil and even molasses. A measured amount of fuel is then injected into the cylinder while under compression, which ignites immediately to drive the piston down, creating the most efficient power known to man. This engine depends on the high temperatures of the highly compressed air (500 to 600 pounds per square inch) to ignite the fuel oil charge as it is injected into the combustion chamber during the early part of the working stroke; the amount injected depending on the load, and controlled by the governor.

The first Diesel engine (stationary) in the United States was built by a company organized by Adolph Busch, of St. Louis, Missouri, who had purchased the first American Diesel license in 1896. The engine was a 2-cylinder 60 horsepower unit weighing about 400 pounds per horsepower. The first Diesel tractor in the United States was built in 1931 by the Caterpillar Tractor Company, Peoria, Illinois. It was of the track-type powered with a 4-cylinder Diesel engine and made use of a 2-cylinder gasoline engine for starting. By 1950 Diesel engines were widely used in locomotives, ships, trucks, buses, tractors, industrial machines and to power electric generators ranging in size from one to thousands of horsepower.

Caterpillar was first tractor to be Diesel powered in 1931. Mr. Diesel mysteriously disappeared from a steamer crossing the English Channel in 1913.

In 1913 Mr. Diesel mysteriously disappeared from a steamer on which he was crossing the English Channel during a lecture tour, endeavoring to get acceptance of his radically new engine. His body was never found. His important papers were also missing. 172

Philosopher of Physics
ALBERT
EINSTEIN

Albert Einstein didn't learn to talk until he was five.

Albert Einstein would have been considered mentally retarded today, for he did not talk until he was almost five years of age. Yet he won the Nobel prize in 1921. Einstein evolved the theory of relativity, Brownian motions of heat particles, a light quantum theory, and a law of photo electric effect, among others.   173

On March 16, 1926 Dr. Robert H. Goddard fired his first liquid-filled rocket, (now on display at the Smithsonian Institute in Washington, D.C.). It was launched from a farm at Auburn, Massachusetts, was airborne for 2½ seconds, and traveled only 184 feet. It was, however, the first successful launching of the same type of rocket that has since carried man to the moon and instruments to Venus and Mars. Goddard predicted this in 1929 and was then referred to as "that crazy professor who wants to go to the moon."   174

R.H. Goddard and his first rocket.
In 1929 Goddard was referred to as "that crazy professor who wants to go to the moon."

Wernher Von Braun was a German-born rocket wizard who designed Hitler's V-2 missiles and launched the U.S. space program. An engineering prodigy and son of the Weimar Republic's Minister of Agriculture, Von Braun commenced experimenting with Goddard's rockets when he was 15 years old and when only 20, received a grant from the German Army to experiment with missiles in 1932. As head of a rocket center in Peenemunde, he developed the long-range V-2's, more than 1,000 of which rained on London-area targets in the last year of World War II. In January 1945 Von Braun and his team of more than 100 engineers surrendered to the advancing Americans and eventually migrated to the U.S. to form a nucleus of the space research unit in Huntsville, Alabama. There Von Braun developed Explorer 1, the first U.S. space satellite, launched in 1958. Later, as the National Aeronautics and Space Administration's top rocket expert, he produced the Saturn 5 rocket that sent astronauts to the moon. Von Braun, all his life, persued rocketry with a vengeance, the U.S. Government often slow to accept his ideas. He died of cancer in 1977, age 65.   175

In 1945 VonBraun and his helpers surrendered to the Americans, but it took him years to convince U.S. authorities that he could send men to the moon.

The First Snowmobile

Rural mail carriers and doctors bought these Ford Ski-Track Kits by the thousands.

The granddaddy of snowmobiles is the Model T Ford. With snowtracks attached to the rear axle and a special attachment to the front, it traversed snowy terrains. Thousands of these kits, to make snowmobiles out of Ford cars, were sold to mail carriers and family doctors in the northern states. One can be seen at the Harold Warp Pioneer Village, at Minden, in south central Nebraska.   176

HAROLD WARP PIONEER VILLAGE FOUNDATION
Minden, Neb. 68959

Carl Eliason attached a Johnson outboard and some Ford parts to a toboggan to patent the first snow-mobile in 1927.

Carl Eliason, a Sayner, Wisconsin lumber dealer, invented the snowmobile. He put together a Johnson outboard motor, a Ford radiator, a Ford differential and belted cleats on a toboggan guided by a pair of skis. He patented it in 1927. His patent ran out before the snowmobile became popular in the 1970s. The largest collection of 40 different early snowmobiles can be seen at the Harold Warp Pioneer Village at Minden in south central Nebraska.   177

HAROLD WARP PIONEER VILLAGE FOUNDATION
Minden, Neb. 68959

Thomas Edison

An overdue gas bill prompted Edison to invent the electric light.

Thomas A. Edison told B.C. Forbes on October 16, 1920, that his quest for an electric light was prompted by his gas being shut off. "I was paying a sheriff $5 a day to postpone a judgment on my small factory," said Mr. Edison, recalling the days of 40 years ago. "Then came the gas man, and because I could not pay his bill promptly, he cut off my gas. I was in the midst of certain very important experiments, and to have the gas people plunge me into darkness made me so mad that I at once began to read up on gas technique and economics, and resolved I would try to see if electricity couldn't be made to replace gas lights and give those gas people a run for their money. I stuck to my search for four years, but I was so poor an economist that I didn't hurt them at all except lately, 40 years after having my gas cut off."   178

Edison developed direct current, but Sam Insull, Edison's helper, sold J.P. Morgan on developing alternating current. Edison then got out of electricity (except for developing the storage battery) saying "electricity has grown too old for me."

Thomas Edison's first electric light consisted of a piece of cotton sewing thread fastened inside a tube from which the air had been pumped out, October 21, 1879. It stayed lit forty hours before it burned out. Then on December 17, 1880, Thomas Edison set up the Edison Electric Co. to furnish electricity for lighting New York City. In June of 1828 Joseph Henry of Albany, New York had discovered how to harness electricity to create a magnet that would make electric motors possible. 179

After inventing the electric light, Edison had to design a dynamo, wiring, fuses, and meter.

Magnetic ore separation.

Poured cement houses.

Lifetime storage battery.

When Samuel Insull, whom Edison had brought from England in 1880 to be his secretary, made a deal with J.P. Morgan and Thompson-Houston, to set up "General Electric Company" on April 15, 1892, leaving Edison's name out, who had actually invented and founded this industry, Edison turned "white as a sheet." Edison proceeded to sell his "Edison stock" which netted him a little over a million dollars, bitterly saying "Electricity has grown too old for me."

He invested his million dollars in a magnetic iron mining venture in the New Jersey highlands, but he was 50 years too early with his "Taconite" method of mining as labor and ore was still plentiful and cheap. (Edison's magnetic method of making "Taconite" became a reality in 1960.) Broke, in 1902 Edison came down out of the New Jersey highlands to start all over again with development of Portland cement from iron ore slag and commenced building cement houses using prefabricated forms. He then proceeded to build another fortune with his talking moving pictures, Edison phonographs, Edison dictating machines and Edison "lifetime" storage batteries. He died in 1932 while trying to make rubber from milk-weeds and dandelions. He never believed in exercise, saying his body was only to carry his brain. 180

Charles F. Kettering

His mother's 1913 Christmas present sparked the sale of millions of Delco light plants to farmers everywhere.

Charles F. Kettering, an Ohio farm boy and country school teacher who invented the K-W automobile ignition system and the self-starter for cars, also built the "Delco Light Plant" that revolutionized lighting on the farm. He had built one of these and installed it himself in his mother's farm home, as a Christmas present in 1913, to replace her kerosene lamp. Other farmers wanted them, so he formed a company to make Delco Light Plants in 1916. The first year he sold two and a half million dollars worth of them with 16 clear glass storage batteries, 10 electric outlets, 10 light bulbs, also one power outlet where specified by the purchaser for $570, installed. Millions of these one cylinder gasoline starting-kerosene running 32 volt home lighting plants were sold to farmers during the late 'teens and 1920s. A few families used an electric washing machine and flat iron with them, but the majority of farmers used them only for lighting. The plant would have to be run three or four hours per day to keep the sixteen glass enclosed battery cells charged up and the ruggedness of this kerosene engine was amazing. The advent of rural electrification in the 1930s and 1940s ended the need for a Delco light plant in the cellar.   181

Out near Red Wing, Minnesota in 1924 the first experimental rural power line was built to not only light the house, but to pump water, grind feed, saw wood and run the waffle iron. Electric refrigerators had not yet been invented. The stipulation was that if enough farmers could be persuaded to tie in, the kilowatt hour cost could be cut in half. (To 5 cents or less.) It was an immediate success. By 1928 a half million farmers were using electric power and by 1940 a million farmers were lighting hen-houses and plugging in refrigerators with electricity.   182

The first rural power line went out from Red Wing, Minnesota to nearby farmers in 1924.

It was just a cardboard tube.

The first flashlight (a cardboard tube with metal fittings) was made by the American Electric & Novelty Mfg. Co., New York City, in 1898.   183

Designed to spot surveyors miles away, it wound up putting theatre actors in the "Lime-Light".

In 1825 a British officer named Thomas Drummond invented a lighting system of intense brilliance that utilized an oxyhydrogen flame directed on a cylinder of lime. Although his invention was designed to make distant surveying stations visible, the new "lime light" was quickly adapted for theater use, to put the leading player — the center of attention on the state — "in the limelight."

184

While Wilhelm Rŏetgen, Physics Professor at Wŭrzburg University in Bavaria was conducting cathode-ray experiments in his darkened laboratory, a cardboard across the room covered with chemical, was noted to cast a green glow. When Rŏetgen put his hand in front of the cardboard, to his amazement, it showed only a shadow of his hand, but there was a clear picture of the bones in his hand. Rŏetgen had no idea what these rays were, so he named them x-rays, x being the unknown quantity. Rŏetgen invented the electric light tube that emitted short invisible X-rays that penetrated solids at varying degrees, depending on intensity; it was one of the pioneering advancements in medical history. He refused to patent it and never made a penny from his discovery of X-rays. One of his original 1895 X-ray tubes is on display at the Harold Warp Pioneer Village, Minden, Nebraska.

185

The bones in his hand showed, when Wilhelm Rŏetgen happened to put his hand in front of a cardboard he had mixed chemicals on. He had no idea what they were, so he named them X-rays.

Watt — This is one of several electrical terms that come from the names of scientists. Watt comes from James Watt, a Scottish engineer. Volt is named after Alessandro Volta, a 17th-century Italian physicist. Ampere comes from French physicist and mathematician Andre Ampre. Ohm is from George Ohm, a German physicist of the 17th century.

186

James Watt

Greenleaf Whittier Pickard

Radio waves were a chance discovery in 1906.

By 1920 kids everywhere were building crystal sets on oatmeal boxes and cigar boxes.

It was discovered in 1906 by Dunwoody and Pickard that carborundum and silicon crystals could pick up radio signals and Reginald Fessenden made the first radio broadcast that year at Brant Rock, Massachusetts, but it was not until 1920, when KDKA at Pittsburgh, Pennsylvania first went on the air, that "Catwhiskers", "Crystals" and other parts appeared in Sears and Wards catalogs to make crystal radio receivers. It was quite a thrill for the neighbors to put on the extra headset while the "radio bug" fiddled with the catwhisker until voice or music could be heard above the mysterious squeaks, growls and static interference. No batteries or electrical connections were necessary with these early crystal sets. Several broadcasting stations across the country quickly followed KDKA in 1920. All receiving sets were then "homemade" with parts purchased from a mail order catalog and a wire coil was wound on an empty oatmeal box.   187

The first radio broadcast of U.S. Presidential election results was KDKA, Pittsburgh, PA, in November 1920 when Harding beat Cox.   188

The first radio broadcast of a major league game came over radio station KDKA, August 5, 1921.
189

Lee DeForest's invention of sound on film brought him only grief.

DeForest, who invented the radio vacuum tube, also invented the first sound on film in 1920, "Phonofilm". From 1923 to 1926 he offered his phonofilm to one studio after the other with no success. Then in 1926 Warner Bros. decided to use Edison's phonograph records synchronized with the film and folks liked it. By then Western Electric and Bell Laboratories had found ways to get around DeForest's "Phonofilm" patents and he realized nothing but grief from this invention.   190

In 1915 Le DeForest was indicted by the U.S. Postal Department for using the mails to defraud, claiming his radio vacuum tube "a worthless piece of glass".

Lee DeForest, inventor of the radio vacuum tube in 1907, was indicted in 1915 for using the mails to defraud, because he claimed his tube would make it possible to hear human voices across oceans. The government prosecutor called DeForest's vacuum tube "a worthless piece of glass". He was acquitted in 1916 by jury trial. Within a year thereafter the human voice was broadcast by using his patented vacuum tube from Arlington, Virginia to Honolulu. He also coined the word "Broadcast", but died a poor man, June 30, 1961, after spending most of his life defending his patents in court cases.   191

The one man most responsible for advancement in radio circuitry was Major Edwin H. Armstrong. He invented feedback, key to tube receivers and transmitters, in 1912. While in the Army in 1918, he invented the superheterodyne receiver, the basic circuit of most radios. This was followed in 1922 by the super-regenerative receiver, the most sensitive single-tube circuit known. In 1933 Major Armstrong capped his career by inventing frequency modulation (FM). He participated in many other pioneer efforts, such as the earliest transatlantic amateur communications by 1BCG.   192

Ed Armstrong was not only an Army Major, but also a radio genius.

Dave Sarnoff not only reported the unsinkable Titanic sinking, but went on to build "RCA".

A young man named David Sarnoff, in a tenement house in New York, made the first practical use of wireless telegraph when he contacted the supposedly unsinkable Titanic when it was sinking after hitting an iceberg on its maiden voyage across the Atlantic in 1912. As David Sarnoff grew older, he put together the Radio Corporation of America (RCA) with the help of Joe Kennedy (President John Kennedy's father) by purchasing various radio manufacturers, including the Victor Talking Machine Company (in 1929) and remained RCA's chief officer until his death in 1971.   193

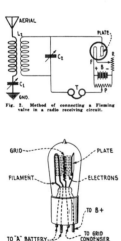

They used their initials for call letters.

When commercial radio stations first went on the air in the mid 1920s, they were allowed to pick their own call letters, preceded by the letter "W" for wireless, or some other letter, approved by the U.S. Dept. of Commerce. Here are some of the call letters selected:

WLS — Chicago, for "World's Largest Store" (Sears)

WGN — Chicago, for World's Greatest Newspaper" (Chicago Tribune)

WOW — Omaha for "Woodmen of the World" (Insurance)

WLW — Cincinnati for "World's Leading Wireless" (Crosley Radio Corp.)

KMMJ — Clay Center, Nebr. "M.M. Johnson Incubator Co."

WCFL — "Chicago Federation of Labor"   194

Minden, Neb. 68959

In 1883 Thomas Edison discovered that the heat from an electric light bulb gave off electrified particles. This phenomenen was called the "Edison effect," but he did nothing with it. In 1904, J.A. Fleming of England produced the "Edison effect" by heating a filament in a vacuum tube. Then he used the electrified particles (electrons) to carry current from another circuit across the gap in the tube, which he named the "Fleming Valve", more recently called a "diode". In 1906 Lee DeForest transformed the Fleming Valve into what he named an "Audion" (later called a "Triode") by inserting a grid of fine wire mesh between the filament and the plate of the diode. The Edison effect plus Fleming's Valve, the "Diode" has also become the common way to convert alternating current (AC) into direct current (DC) and for charging batteries. The alternating current (AC) is divided between two circuits. One circuit heats the filament; the other circuit is connected across the gap in the diode, causing the current to flow only one way, from filament to plate (DC).   195

Fig. 2. Method of connecting a Fleming valve in a radio receiving circuit.

J.A. Armstrong and Lee DeForest used "Edison's effect" as a base for their inventions.

HAROLD WARP PIONEER VILLAGE FOUNDATION
Minden, Neb. 68959

The first radio telephone system in the world was set up between Catalina Island and the California coast in 1920.   196

First radio report of car theft 1928.

When the city of Chicago started putting radios in police cars in the early 1920s, two brothers commenced making radios that were hidden under the dash so gangsters and bootleggers could monitor police calls. When this market was saturated the Motorola "under the dash" radio was introduced in 1930 for $30 by Paul and Joe Galvin.   197

Motorola car radio 1930.

Evolution of the CB radio for inter vehicle communications got its start with the world's first police call placed in Detroit, April 7th, 1928. Walter Vogler of Detroit's police department reported a car theft to police cars with receivers — transmitters were not yet in use in police cars.   198

Henry Field wouldn't let Bert Presba give his prepared speech over KFNF.

The first radio commercial message was broadcast in the Midwest over station KFNF, at Shenandoah, Iowa, in the fall of 1927, for the Aladdin Kerosene Mantle Lamp Company of Chicago. Bert S. Presba, Aladdin sales manager, had taken a train from Chicago to Shenandoah to try and convince the station owner to read his sales message over the air. Henry Field, who had gone on the air with his station KFNF in 1924 to sell his own nursery stock, told Presba that he wouldn't put a message over his station for anyone else for less than $500. Presba told Field that this was to be a test and he was prepared to pay $500. Field then told Presba to set the Aladdin lamp on his desk and light it. Henry Field ignored Bert Presba's prepared script, talked about the bright light this lamp gave that stood on his desk, which had been invented by Victor Johnson of Chicago. This first commercial brought in over 2200 inquiries.   199

After kids had been building their own radio receivers for years, RCA offered the first "Radiola III" for $35 in 1924.

In 1924 RCA introduced its first successful radio in a box. It had two "peanut" tubes and plug-in sockets for two headsets. The Radiola III required three 1½ volt batteries and two 22½ volt "B" batteries. It was a regenerative receiver with one detector and one audio stage. It cost $35.00. "Headset" receivers cost $3.00 a pair and batteries were also extra, as well as a copper wire aerial that was strung between two roof gables, or from the top of a windmill tower. Radio reception was nationwide.

200

HAROLD WARP
PIONEER VILLAGE
Minden, Neb. 68959   FOUNDATION

Albers brothers' wind charger put Gene McDonald's Zenith radio in thousands of farm homes.

ZENITH AND THE FOUR WINDS
REVOLUTIONIZED
FARM RADIO
ASK ZENITH OWNERS
ZENITH
LONG DISTANCE
FARM RADIO

A Zenith radio ad.

In 1927 John and Gerhardt Albers, farm brothers in their 20s, living near Cherokee, Iowa, fastened a 6 volt electric automobile generator to their windmill to keep their 6 volt radio battery charged up. It worked, they patented it, and they had made a few for their friends and neighbors for $44.50 each, using old 6 volt auto generators, when Gene McDonald, head of the then struggling Zenith Radio Company in Chicago, learned what these boys were doing. McDonald knew the big market for radios at that time was on the farm, where no electricity was then available, with no means of recharging a battery. So he sent Karl Hassel, one of the developers of the Zenith radio, out to see the Albers brothers on April 5, 1935, together with a Mr. Freese. Hassel later said, "When we arrived we found the so-called Wincharger factory heated with a little coal stove. The crude Wincharger they were building wasn't even equipped with a governor, so we pointed out that if they would permit us to finance them and put in modern machinery we could reduce the price to $10 to $15 on an improved model." They they did. Gene McDonald gave the Albers boys an order for 50,000 Winchargers that he sold to farmers for $10 each with a Zenith radio. This carried the Zenith Radio Company through the depression years, and on to undreamed of sales of Zenith radios as the years went by. Albers brothers' Winchargers had become a common sight on farms everywhere by 1942, but when rural electric lines were strung across the country during the 1940s it ended the need for Winchargers. 201

They made Ford sun-visors and battery trickle chargers before radios.

Ford Windshield Sun-Visors were being made at 4700 W. Armitage Ave., Chicago by Mr. Grigsby and Bill Grunow in 1924 when RCA started making earphone radiolas. That year Grigsby-Grunow started making Trickle-Chargers for car batteries, being used to run Radiolas. Mr. Jensen came to them with a "Dynamic Speaker" he had developed to replace earphones. They decided to build a floor standing cabinet around it and put a radio inside. Grigsby-Grunow's "Majestic" radio, costing $187, was an immediate success. In 1926 they moved a mile west, near the Belt R.R. yards, even using rail cars as warehouse space. Majestic shares on the stock market soared far beyond their value, but crashed with the stock market in October, 1929. Ironically, folks were still listening to Majestic radios in their living rooms 30 years later.

Grigsby Grunow really went to town with their Dynamic speaker in a cabinet radio.

In the 1930s Bill Grunow came back with his farm-raised chickens, cut up and sold by the piece in his own "Val-O-Will" Chicago stores, while Eugene McDonald took over the former "Majestic" factory to make his "Zenith" radios. (See #201)   202

HAROLD WARP
PIONEER VILLAGE
Minden, Neb. 68959 FOUNDATION

Admiral Byrd took a Jacobs 32 volt wind generator to the Antarctic in 1934. Twenty years later, on July 14, 1954, on entering the Bay of Whales in Little America Antarctica, nothing was visible of Byrd's former headquarters. They were about to turn around when suddenly the crow's nest lookout, peering through his glass, shouted he saw a pole with a propeller spinning on top of it. Bud Waite grabbed his glasses, climbed the mast and yelled, "That's it, that's the electric generator I put up twenty years ago!" It had withstood the onslaught of the Antarctic wastes for twenty years and was still spinning above the buried buildings of Byrd's 1929 and 1934 Little America Headquarters. An identical 32 volt generator weighing 400 pounds, with blades on an 11½ foot arc can be seen at the Pioneer Village.   203

Admiral Byrd's Jacobs wind generator still spinning when Byrd arrived in Antarctic again 20 years later.

Sharkley, Brittain and Bardeen's minute transistor discovery in 1948 made miniature radios possible.

HAROLD WARP
PIONEER VILLAGE
Minden, Neb. 68959 FOUNDATION

The first miniature radio that could be held in the palm of the hand was made by the Bulova Watch Company in 1950. What had made this small "solid state" radio possible was the discovery of the

When 88 in 1977, Dr. Zworykin, Russian immigrant who developed the T.V. picture tube stated: "My idea was an instrument so doctors could see inside the human body, not crime and violence."

minute transistor developed in 1948 by Wm. Shackley, Walter Brittain and John Bardeen, with Bell Telephone Laboratories, who had discovered how to replace radio vacuum tubes by passing an electric current through a particle of germanium. 204

Known as the iconoscope and kinescope, the "picture tube" was developed by Dr. Vladimir Zworykin in the late 1920s, who fled to the U.S. when the communists took over Russia. He patented over 120 electronics devices. In 1977 when 88, he stated: "My first idea for television was a useful instrument so doctors could see inside the human body, where their eyes could not look, not commercial exploitation. The pictures from Mars and the moon are the medium's greatest accomplishments. This glorification of crime and violence is no good for our children. Aside from news, nature shows and wild life, I find nothing else worth viewing." *Gleaned from Grit 12-4-77.* 205

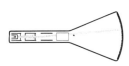

DuMont was first with a T.V. network in 1941, but Sarnoff's RCA soon overtook him.

The first television picture was transmitted by Philo T. Farnsworth in San Francisco in 1927. He applied for a patent when he was 18. In 1931 Allen Balcom Du Mont perfected the first commercially practical cathode-ray tube, when he was 30. The first public viewing of television was at the Chicago World's Fair in 1933. Du Mont commenced selling a giant 14 inch tube receiver in 1938 and offered the first network of three TV broadcasting stations, in New England, in 1941. Du Mont was soon left far behind by David Sarnoff's better financed RCA (Radio Corporation of America). 206

Test patterns of the war zone, 15 minutes each evening, comprised T.V., 1941 to 1945.

RCA came out with a five inch model television in 1941. Very few were sold due to lack of broadcasting stations. Sales did not commence to climb until 1948, when network broadcasting was inaugurated by NBC (National Broadcasting Company). 207

The very first television broadcast over NBC was August 21, 1939, showing a major league baseball game. The first color TV was broadcast over NBC August 26, 1951 from KDKA in Pittsburg, showing the Brooklyn Dodgers at Ebbets Field. 208

Gernsback coined the word "television" in one of his 1879 science fiction stories.

The term television was coined by a Russian, Constantin Perskyi, presenting a technical paper in Paris in 1900 and an American science-fiction writer, Hugo Gernsback, popularized the word. Earlier, in 1879, Britian's Sir William Crookes had begun experiments with the cathode rays needed for electronic television, and by 1897, Germany's Karl Ferdinand Braun managed to control the electron scanning beam in a cathode-ray tube. 209

In 1884, Germany's Paul Gottlieb Nipkow developed a mechanical scanning device that could transmit images over short distances. The basic idea was to direct the light reflecting off a subject through holes in a spinning disc – much like the shutter of a motion picture camera. But instead of directing the exposures to light-sensitive film, the image receptor was a photoelectric cell. 210

Spinning discs with holes in them broadcast images over short distances in the 1920s.

Mechanical TV broadcasts commenced in the 1920s. Britain's John Logie Baird introduced a working system in 1925, a development paralleled in the U.S. by Charles Francis Perkins. The latter, a lone inventor who also developed the modern movie projector, became a broadcaster in 1928 when the federal government issued permits for experimental telecasts. His two experimental stations aired movie films, which Americans could view through the one inch peepholes of homebuilt, spinning-disc receivers. 211

Developments in all-electronic TV that were to make the spinning disc mechanical system

Dr. Vladimir Zworykin

Electronic "Boob-Tubes" made spinning discs obsolete in 1936 for T.V. broadcasting and reception.

T.V. didn't take off until 1946, when 6000 sets were sold in the U.S. tuned to 9 broadcasting stations nationwide.

Franklin Roosevelt opened the 1939 New York World's Fair by television to less than 200 T.V. receivers in entire U.S.A.

The first T.V. commercial cost Bulova watch company $9 in 1941.

obsolete, were perfected simultaneously in 1931 by Philo T. Farnsworth, a Midwestern whiz-kid, and RCA's Russian-born Vladimir K. Zworykin (the independent David and the corporate Goliath would fight patent battles for years to come). Ironically, the British Broadcasting Corp. embraced the boobtube in 1936 – three years before NBC's World's Fair telecast and five years before the U.S. Federal Communications Commission okayed our present NTSC (National Television System Committee) method of telecasting.   212

When NBC began regular telecasts in 1939, pioneer Allen B. DuMont was already broadcasting in New England. He was also actually selling a "giant" 14-inch tube receiver. TV didn't take off until after World War II, however. Some 6000 receivers were produced and sold in 1946, with nine stations on the air – including the soon-defunct DuMont network, where Jackie Gleason and his "Honeymooners" made their 1955 debut as a skit on the original "Jackie Gleason Show."   213

The first Presidential speech by television was April 30, 1939, when Franklin Roosevelt opened the New York World's Fair. There were then less than 200 television receiving sets in the U.S. The first television broadcast of a major league baseball game was August 21, 1939, when NBC first started regular TV broadcasts.   214

The first baseball game on television was broadcast over NBC May 17, 1939, when Lou Gehrig played his last game.   215

The first TV commercial was broadcast over WNBT in New York. The announcer focused on the face of a Bulova watch 10 minutes past 10 P.M.. The ad cost $9 in 1941.   216

Oil filled magnifiers were sold to enlarge the small picture on early T.V. sets.

In April 1939 there were less than 200 television receiving sets in the U.S. and in 1946 only 6000 TV sets were sold. But by 1950, 140 brands of TVs were producing more than five million sets a year. The golden age of TV was in full swing with classic programs such as "The Milton Berle Show" (1948) and "I Love Lucy" (1951) appearing in glorious – and live – black and white. Color TVs and videotape wouldn't become available until 1946. By 1990 there was a TV in virtually every home and a VCR (Video Cassette Recorder) in three out of five. Wide-screen High Definition TV was also being developed in 1990. *Gleaned from an article in Popular Mechanics by Stephen A. Booth.*   217

Samuel F.B. Morse, a Yale graduate who became a famous portrait painter, sketched up the idea of a telegraph in 1832 while crossing the Atlantic from France, on the *Sully*. He said to the captain, "Remember, when you hear of the magnetic telegraph, it was invented on your ship." But it was not until 1861, 29 years later that the first Morse Code telegraph message was sent across the U.S. That also ended the need for the transcontinental Pony Express. His Morse Code had the shortest symbols for the most often used letters (one dot for E).   218

Samuel Morse predicted his invention of the telegraph 29 years before he patented it.

Electrical wizard Elisha Gray accepted $100,000 in 1892 to concede invention of the telephone to Alexander Graham Bell, who had filed for a patent 2/14/76 for the same instrument, on the same day as Gray.

Elisha Gray, an electrical wizard, and Graham Bell, an elocutionist, filed patent applications in the U.S. Patent office on the same day, February 14, 1876, on the same instrument, intended to carry the human voice over wires. After years of litigation, payment of $100,000 finally was offered and accepted by Gray in 1892 to concede the invention to Mr. Bell. Thomas Edison, however, was the man who really developed the telephone into a practical workable instrument for carrying the human voice over the telephone wires. On April 27, 1877 Edison filed the first patent on a carbon button transmitter, separate from the receiver. Prior to that, the same instrument was used for both talking and listening. The telephone is still made basically the same as when Edison perfected it.   219

Undertaker Strowger invented the dial phone in 1889 to prevent competitors from stealing his customers (corpses).

The dial telephone was invented by Mr. A.B. Strowger, a St. Louis undertaker. In 1889, he put it together in a collar box. He suspected his competitors of bribing telephone operators.   220

In 1887 a friend gave Thomas Edison a "wheel of life" machine. When he spun the wheel he watched the bear dance as the cards slipped by the peep hole. Edison took out his notebook and commenced sketching the first true moving pictures on a continuous film synchronized with his phonograph. He showed the first talking pictures two years later in his laboratory in 1898.   221

Edison sketched the first movie machine in 1896 when he saw a bear dance, as he peeped through a hole in a box with cards fastened to a spinning wheel.

Thomas Edison invented the phonograph in 1877 using a tinfoil cylinder. He did nothing with it, as he was busy with electricity and in 1888 Charles Tainter and C.A. Bell patented a wax cylinder to go on an Edison phonograph. This stopped phonograph development until Edison's original phonograph patent expired. Johnson perfected a flat disc wax record in 1901 when Tainter and Bell's patent expired. He then commenced making Victor talking machines.   222

Edison's original phonograph.

When Tainter and Bell patented a wax cylinder in 1888 to go on Edison's 1877 (tinfoil) phonograph, development remained dormant until 1901 when both patents had expired.

Twelve years after Edison had invented the phonograph, he stated in 1888, "I don't want the phonograph sold for amusement purposes. It is not a toy." He was then developing the Edison dictating machine and Edison record shaver so his records could be reused for office dictation rather than shorthand dictation. (The writer used Edison's dictating machine and record shaver for many years. They were both spring wound by using a crank and had no electrical connections.)   223

1903 Victor

Thomas Edison said in 1888 "I don't want the phonograph sold for amusement purposes. It is not a toy."

Two years after Edison said he didn't want his phonograph used as a toy, the first "business" use in 1890 was in a saloon, for a nickel a dozen people could listen at one time.

In 1890, to the chagrin of Mr. Edison, the first "business" use of his phonograph was in a saloon, where customers were required to put in a nickel to listen to one of a dozen sets of headphones all attached to the same talking machine. It was played over 20,000 times the first six months. 224

In 1904 Edison started making Edison phonographs, using a non-replaceable diamond needle. In 1907 he commenced putting the horn inside the phonograph case, to resemble a piece of furniture and in 1910 switched to flat disc records. During the next ten years Edison sold millions of his phonographs and records ... and so did Victor, that in 1929 became a part of RCA, put together by Joe Kennedy (President John Kennedy's dad) for David Sarnoff. 225

1910 Edison

Edison's phonograph finally wound up as part of RCA, put together by President John F. Kennedy's father, Joe, in 1929.

One man is responsible for perfecting the Virtuoso, Henry K. Sandell (1878-1948), a Nebraska Sandhills farmer. The self-playing violin and piano combination was electrically operated, controlled and directed by a specially punched paper tape that cost a nickel to play. The Mills Novelty Company of Chicago acquired the manufacturing rights. Between 1905 and 1928 they made 5,500 of these instruments. None of the punched paper tape rolls have been made since 1931, at which time the perforating equipment was scrapped. In the late 1920s, the nickel phonograph "Jukebox" began to replace it. 226

A Nebraska sandhill farmer is responsible for the "Virtuoso" that played both a violin and piano for a nickel, introduced in 1905.

The first piano, or harpsichord is credited to Christofori of Italy in 1709. It was really a harp in a horizontal position with leather covered hammers and a keyboard action. It took 50 years for the general public to accept the upright piano that was developed by Hawkins in 1800. 227

The first piano in 1709 was merely a harp laid on its side, struck with "keys" in place of fingers.

Oersted

His electrified wire made the compass spin.

Joseph Henry

His "Electro-Magnet" could pick up 750 pounds when he attached a battery to a silk covered fine copper wire wound, many layers, around an iron bar. In 1831 Michael Faraday ran the first electric motor, using Henry's theory.

An English brick layer made the first Portland Cement on his kitchen stove, patented it in 1824. It is still the most widely used cement today.

Genuine Linoleum RUGS

Fred Walton invented linoleum in 1860 when he noticed a can of linseed oil got a scum on top if he left the lid off.

In 1820 a Danish physicist, Hans Christian Oersted discovered a relationship between electricity and magnetism when he made the compass spin by holding an electrified wire close to it. William Sturgeon, son of an English shoemaker took Oersted's discovery one step farther and wrapped wire around a horseshoe magnet. When he passed electricity through the wire, the "electromagnet" as he called it, would lift 20 times its own weight. Ten years later Joseph Henry, an American physicist, wound layer upon layer of silk covered copper wire around an iron bar, which greatly increased the magnet's power. By attaching a battery to the wire Henry's magnet lifted 750 lbs. William Sturgeon went on to build the first successful rotary electric motor, based on the principles of Michael Faraday. 228

Joseph Aspdin, an English bricklayer, mixed together some clay and limestone, and burned it to a clinker on his kitchen stove in 1824. He patented it as "Portland Cement" because its color resembled that of a stone quarried on the Isle of Portland on the English Coast. The chemical ingredients are silica, aluminum oxide, iron oxide, and lime properly proportioned and burned into clinkers at 2,700° F., then ground to a fine powder. When properly mixed with aggregate and water, it becomes harder with age. Portland cement, commonly called concrete, should not be confused with limestone plaster, used as far back as 4,500 years ago by the Egyptians in building pyramids, some of which are still in good condition. 229

Linoleum was invented by accident in 1860 when an Englishman named Frederick Walton noticed that linseed oil oxidized on the surface of open paint cans. He spread a mixture of the oxidized oil, resin, and ground cork on a burlap backing and cured the mess for weeks in large ovens. American factories started turning it out in 1909. 230

WOODCUT BOOKPLATE AND ITS IMPRESSION

Wood cuts produced most pictures prior to 1925, carved with sharp knives, under a microscope by thousands of trained artisions, called "engravers". Etchings were the opposite. Ink was deposited on paper from crevices cut into a stone surface).

Wood engravings were used for illustrations for hundreds of years. Only since 1900 have metal etchings all but made the engraver's trade a lost art. Wood engravings reached their peak between 1875 and 1925, when magazines and mail order catalogs flourished with the delivery of mail everywhere in the country. To make a wood cut the artist first draws the picture in reverse, on a smooth surface of the end grain of a block of wood that is "type high". Then with the use of a magnifying glass the wood is tediously cut away by hand with knives and chisels, where no pencil marks appear on the surface of the wood. Thus, when "inked", the wood surface that is not cut away deposits the ink onto the paper that the wood cut comes in contact with. Some wood engravers became so highly skilled at their art that some of these old wood cuts still surpass the reproduction of present day metal engravings. 231

HAROLD WARP
PIONEER VILLAGE
Minden, Neb. 68959 FOUNDATION

Kids got action for their money when over 200 different mechanical bank patents were issued between 1869 and 1907.

After the Civil War children were persuaded to put their pennies in mechanical banks, that performed tricks, to induce thrift. This was long before slot machines, known as "one armed bandits" were invented to induce people to part with their nickels. Over 200 mechanical bank patents were issued between 1869, when the first "Halls Excelsior" was introduced and 1907 and the last, when a penny would make a bear pop out of the top of a tree trunk when Teddy Roosevelt shot the penny into a hole in the tree. 232

HAROLD WARP
PIONEER VILLAGE
Minden, Neb. 68959 FOUNDATION

Vacuum cleaners didn't become popular until streets were paved and the dust quit flying from horses hooves.

Vacuum cleaners had not yet been invented when horseless carriages and flying machines first began to make the dust fly in 1903. The first vacuum cleaner, a huge cumbersome contraption that was pumped by hand, was introduced in 1905, by Wm. Doe of San Francisco. 233

HAROLD WARP
PIONEER VILLAGE
Minden, Neb. 68959 FOUNDATION

Introduced in 1890, reintroduced in 1950.

Ice harvesting was big business.

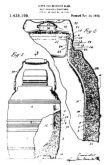

Lord Kelvin (Wm. Thomson) He made the self contained refrigerator possible in 1925.

1,435,199.

Vic Johnson should have taken the royalty offered him.

An 1890 ice box had rotating food shelves. Ice was dropped in the ice compartment at the top when the lid was lifted. The semi-revolving shelf idea was rediscovered by General Electric during the 1950s with great fanfare when they announced the "Lazy Susan" electric refrigerator.   234

Ice harvesting was big business in its day. In 1900 the "Joseph Brek Hardware Catalog" carried twenty-three pages of ice handling equipment, including ice cultivators, planes, plows, saws, chisels, hooks, tongs, carrying bags, iceboxes, etc.   235

The first self-contained electric refrigerator was introduced in 1925. It was an insulated white colored metal Leonard ice box that Kelvinator Company purchased. They installed their Kelvinator electric refrigeration unit in the Leonard box. General Electric's "turret top" sealed unit refrigerator soon followed, some of which were still in use 50 years later.   236

The vacuum bottle was patented by Victor Johnson, in 1919, Patent #1,435,199. Victor Johnson also invented the Aladdin Kerosene Mantle Lamp in 1908. Both were made by him in Chicago, until his death in 1943, when his son Victor S. Johnson moved the factory to Nashville, Tennessee. Several competitors sprung up when Johnson invented the vacuum bottle and on July 8, 1924 the Federal Court ruled the Aladdin patent valid and infringed. One manufacturer sued Johnson for the right to pay him a royalty on each "Little Brown Jug" they manufactured, which Johnson had refused to accept. They finally won the suit in 1931, citing jugs of water in boxes packed with straw for the soldiers during the Civil War. Victor Johnson and Harold Warp, Chicago (plastics manufacturer – Flex-O-Glass, Inc.), were born three miles apart on homesteads near Minden, Nebraska.   237

Rugs made on this loom sold for 10¢ per yard in 1880.

You can learn how to spin.

Elias Howe collected $25 on every Singer sold.

Edward Clark

Singer spent only 11 days inventing the sewing machine. His friend, Clark, perfected it later.

One of the early American crafts still plied at the Harold Warp Pioneer Village in south central Nebraska, is weaving on a 100 year old loom put together with wooden pegs. The original owner was paid 10 cents a yard for rugs made on this loom. 238

Would you like to learn how to spin or weave – a forgotten trade? You can learn to spin and weave like your great grandmother did by watching the ladies practicing these forgotten arts at the Harold Warp Pioneer Village in Minden, in south central Nebraska. 239

In 1846 Elias Howe of Boston invented the handcranked rotary sewing machine, although it was not a true success. Five years later fellow Bostonian Isaac Singer patented an improvement that included a foot treadle, a reciprocating shuttle and adjustable tension for a truly working sewing machine. Howe sued three years later and collected a $25 royalty on each Singer machine manufactured. Later this was reduced to $5, during the patent's 17 year life. 240

Isaac Singer spent only 11 days putting a reciprocating shuttle and a few other improvements on Howe's sewing machine before he filed for a patent in 1851. Edward Clark, who became Singer's half interest (silent) partner in 1852, perfected the Singer sewing machine and marketed it. He also introduced "Clark Sewing Thread" which became the biggest selling sewing thread for the next half century. His grandson, Stephen Carlton Clark, built the "Baseball Hall of Fame" at Cooperstown, New York in 1938, although he did not know how to play baseball. 241

Isaac Singer, an entertainer, lost interest in the sewing machine in 1851, the same year he invented it. He sired 24 children with five women and retired

Isaac Singer sired 24 children, who fought over his $13 million estate.

The rubber roll wringer was patented in 1872, but Sears offered their first washing machine 23 years later.

Parsons and Maytag made twine band cutters for threshing machines before they made washing machines.

The very first washing machine was patented in 1858 but they didn't sell until 50 years later.

When electricity became available, the Thor electric washer, patented in 1910, was preferred by city folks.

to his 115 room "Wigwam" in England in 1873. He died two years later, leaving $13 million that his heirs fought over for many years.   242

The clothes wringer became popular before the washing machine. The adjustable, spring loaded, geared, rubber roll clothes wringer was patented in 1872. This was a quarter of a century before clothes washing machines became popular. Sears Roebuck first offered a washing machine in 1895 and they did not become popular until after 1900.   243

The first hand-operated Maytag washing machine was introduced in 1907 by E.L. Maytag and Mr. Parsons, who were making Parsons Band Cutters and Self Feeders in Newton, Iowa, as labor saving attachments to grain threshers. The washing machine had an agitator hanging from the bottom of the lid resembling a four legged milk stool that was propelled forth and back by a crank fastened to a flywheel on top of the hinged lid. The name was changed to Maytag in 1909, by E.L. Maytag.   244

The first rotary motion washing machine was made in 1859 by Hamilton Erastus Smith, Philadelphia, PA., who obtained patent number 21,909, October 26, 1858, on a perforated cylinder within a wooden shell, revolved with a crank. In 1863, he obtained the first patent on a "self-reversing motion" attachment to the machine, so the cylinder would go forth and back.   245

The first electric powered washing machine was the Thor, marketed by The Hurley Machine Company of Chicago in 1907. A patent number 966,677 was granted August 9, 1910, to Alva J. Fisher, Chicago, on a "drive mechanism for washing machine."   246

In 1842 Cincinnati imposed a $30 luxury tax on bath tubs and Boston forbid their use in winter months.

Although the Greeks and Romans had tubs (mostly public baths) as far back as 1200 B.C., bathtubs did not gain favor in the U.S. until a cast iron tub was introduced in 1870. The first bathtub in the U.S. was built in Cincinnati, Ohio in December 1842. Cincinnati doctors condemned "this outrageous contraption" and a $30 luxury tax was imposed on it. Boston passed a law forbidding the use of a bathtub during the cold months as a health hazard.   247

James B. Liddy

He had the first bed spring in 1853.

One day a New York man took a nap in his "rockaway." It had coiled springs in the seats. He woke up so refreshed that he went to the carriage maker in Watertown, New York and asked the man to make him a similar spring cushion large enough to fit his bed. Thus was made the first bed spring, in 1853, invented that year by James B. Liddy of Watertown, Jefferson County, New York (1828-1921) for his own use and never patented.   248

In 1379 DeVick made his first mechanical clock with two horizontal swinging weights above a weighted escapement wheel. He later added a set of pins on the escapement that made it strike every hour. Prior to 1379, the hourglass, water-clock and sundial were used to tell the time of day.   249

In 1780 the second hand was added to a watch by Dr. Lepine for the purpose of counting the pulse of his patients.   250

DeVick's first mechanical clock in 1379 was very simple.

Discovery of the quartz crystal for watches in 1973 proved quite an innovation.

The first digital watch was made by an American, Hugh Morris, in 1973. Made of a sliver of quartz crystal or an electronic chip, this ingenious computer translates 32,768 cycles or vibrations per second into minutes and hours.   251

The first "safety" razor appeared in 1885.

In 1885 two brothers, Richard and Otto Kampfe, made a safety guard on a section of a straight razor. This was the world's first "Safety Razor" – an invention that made the brothers a fortune. They called it the "Star". Many others followed; the most popular were the "Auto-Shop", "Gem", and "Gillette".   252

King C. Gillette, a 40 year old cork salesman, while on the road in 1895, conceived the idea of making a thin double edged blade that could be thrown away, which he patented, to fit in a holder of his design. By 1902 he had spent $5,000 on his idea and was $12,000 in debt. In 1903 he sold 51 razors and 168 blades. In 1904 sales soared to 90,844 razors and 123,648 blades. Five years later he was on his way to success, with the financial aid of a John Joyce. In World War I every soldier received a Gillette razor, (some of which were still being used 50 years later.) King Gillette, his fortune assured, retired to California and died in 1932. In foreign countries folks still ask for the blades with the man's picture on the package.   253

King C. Gillette conceived the double-edged blade in 1895 while on the road selling cork.

In the early 1930s Col. Schick introduced the truly electric shaver, which had a tiny 7,200 r.p.m. electric motor in the bakelite handle, fastened to an oscillating stainless steel cutting head.   254

Schick Shaver

Tom Edison, in 1870, then 23, made his first successful invention. When asked "how would $40,000 strike you" his answer was "as near fainting as I've ever been."

When Edison was twenty-three he perfected his first really successful invention, the multiple stock ticker, in 1870. He was thinking of asking Western Union Telegraph Company's president, Leffert, $5,000 for it, but instead Edison said, "General, suppose you make me an offer." Leffert then said, "How would forty thousand strike you?" Edison's reply was, "as near fainting as I've ever been." When he cashed this check it was the first time he had ever been inside a bank.   255

First photo of man ever made.

The snapshot you take dates back to the "tintype" developed by Louis Jacque Mande Daguerre, who took the first photograph from his attic window in Paris, France in 1839. 256

In 1890 you had to send the Kodak back to the Eastman factory to have them extract your 100 pictures for $10.00.

In 1884, George Eastman invented roll type film and sold his camera loaded with 100 pictures for $25. It had to be returned to Rochester, N.Y. for developing and refill, to snap another 100 pictures for $10. 257

Stanley twins

They also introduced Stanley tools, still made.

In the 1890s the Stanley twins (who later made the Stanley Steamer) sold George Eastman an improved method of photo-finishing for $800,000 and in 1900 Leo Baekeland (who invented Bakelite) sold Eastman the "velox" photo paper patent for $1 million. There is no accurate information on what David Houston, a North Dakota home-steader, was paid for the many "Kodak" patents Eastman purchased from him between 1881 and 1902. 258

David H. Houston

Could this Dakota farmer have named Eastman's "Kodak" too?

Kodak
Brownie Box Cameras

Did "Kodak" originate from Dakota? David Houston, a homesteader who lived 1½ miles south of Hunter, North Dakota, was granted Patent 248,179, October 11, 1881, for a new camera that used roll film. Houston sold his rights of manufacture and sale to W.H. Walker of Rochester, N.Y. for $700, who subsequently sold it to Eastman. Eastman continued to buy patents from Houston. By 1902 Houston had developed 21 other patents; these included: two roll folding camera, magazine cameras, panoramic cameras, self-loading flash lamp and a daylight loading camera for cartridge film. The name Kodak, it is believed, was derived from "Dakota" and that Eastman obtained the name on agreement with Houston, who died in 1906. 259

George Eastman sent himself this postcard as possible patent protection on his photographic process.

George Eastman, who introduced roll type film and the "Kodak" camera in 1888 never married. When Eastman Kodak was incorporated he stipulated that any profits should be divided equally between Eastman workers and Eastman stockholders. This has been Eastman's policy down through the years. He committed suicide in 1932 at age 78. The note he left said, "My work is done. Why wait?" His home has since become a museum for cameras in Rochester, New York.   260

After World War II three outstanding inventions appeared on the market; the ballpoint pen, television and one minute photographs. At a meeting of the Optical Society of America, on February 22, 1947, Dr. Edwin H. Land, 37 year old President of the Polaroid Corporation, announced he had invented an instant picture process that would allow amateurs to take photos that could be seen in a minute. The first Polaroid Land Camera, Model 95, went on sale November 26, 1948 at the Jordon-Marsh Store in Boston, Massachusetts. Dr. Land, previous to introduction of the instant camera, made his first major scientific discovery while still an under-graduate at Harvard University, which was a commercially practical synthetic light polarizing material in sheet form. He organized the Polaroid Company, of which he was President, Chairman, and Director of Research. The polarizing material was adopted for use in photographic filters and in sunglasses. On December 12, 1957 Land announced that full color pictures had been made in his research laboratory, but it was not until 1963 that Polaroid color film was introduced, that could make color pictures in a minute with a standard Polaroid camera.

First Polaroid

Edwin Land conceived the idea for an instant camera when his granddaughter asked why she had to wait for the picture he took of her. (See #468)

The Eastman Company introduced their own instant picture camera in 1965. Polaroid sued Eastman for patent infringement. The suit dragged on for years, but finally in the late 1980s Polaroid won the suit. The court ordered Eastman to recall the instant cameras they had sold and to stop making instant film, with a judgment to also pay Polaroid many millions of dollars in restitution for patent infringement.   261

Eastman was ordered to pay Poloroid $ millions for patent infringement.

In 1883 Waterman, a salesman, purchased a writing contraption with its own ink reservoir. But when it leaked, ruining a sale, he got an idea for a better one and decided to make it himself. In those days a salesman often wore a vest chain with a small metal container holding a vial of ink in one pocket and a collapsible penholder in the other. Waterman examined several so-called pocket pens and saw that none of them had a mechanism for the sure control of ink flow. He determined to invent one. Applying the principle of capillary attraction, he designed a feed with a groove for air intake and three narrow slits in the bottom of the groove. As air bubbles entered, they pressed against the ink in the barrel and the ink descended through the slits in a uniform flow to the pen point. This device was so novel the Patent Office granted a patent in 1884, only a few months after the filing. Waterman claimed that his new mechanism would "prevent the excessive discharge of the ink when the pen is in use." It was the first practical fountain pen and its three-fissure feed became the standard principle for all other makes produced thereafter. Waterman started assembling his pens on a kitchen table in the rear of a cigar store. In the fall of 1885 he started to advertise. After that Waterman's Ideal rode the road to fortune. The first pens were long tubes with a cap fitted on a projection at the top of a barrel. The cone cap, sliding over the end, did not come until 1899. Color was first used in 1898 with the hexagon holder. L.E. Waterman died in 1901. A self-filling piston replaced the reloading eye dropper in 1903. In a 1908 model the barrel was made with a movable sleeve which exposed a metal bar; by finger pressure the bar squeezed a soft rubber sac. Up to this time there had been no sacs in fountain pens. Waterman, in 1913, introduced a slot big enough to admit the edge of a coin to compress the sac. Later the same year the lever appeared, set in a metal housing attached to the barrel; the lever emptied or filled the sac completely in one stroke.

262

When L.E. Waterman got his patent on a leak-proof fountain pen in 1884 he started putting them together on his kitchen table.

The first patent for a ball point pen was No. 392,046, granted October 30, 1888, to John J. Loud of Weymouth, Mass. Loud used the pen to mark leather fabrics. Another ball point pen device was patented by Van Vechten Riesberg in 1916. Both patents lapsed without improvement renewal.

The man credited with the tricky feat of building a tiny steel ball into a metal nose cone, while leaving just enough room to let ink leak evenly out around the edges, when pressed against paper, was a Hungarian journalist, painter and hypnotist named Laszlo Jozsel Biro, who patented it in Argentina in 1940, when he fled there from Nazi Germany and changed his name to Ladislao Jose Biro. His first ball point pen was a crude writing instrument compared with today's standards. An American, Milton Reynolds, started selling them at Christmas time 1946, when first commercially available after World War II, for $12.50 each, using the slogan "It writes under water". Gimbel's in New York sold them so fast that Christmas, they had them flown in. Reynolds hired pilot Bill Odom to fly him around the world in 1947, handing out Reynolds pens to people wherever we went. The publicity from this escapade was tremendous. Born in Albert Lea, Minn. in 1892, Reynolds died in Mexico City in 1976 at age 84. Biro sold his patent to Eversharp Inc. and Eberhard Fabre Corp., as well as the use of his name, and they in turn sold the name "Bic" to a British concern in 1947, which in turn sold the name to Societe Bic S.A., France, in 1957. In the U.S. the Bic Company changed the name of the pen to Biro in 1982 and by 1986 they had sold over a billion Biro ball points. In 1987 Bic U.S.A. changed the name back to Bic in keeping with their Bic shavers and Bic lighters, and sold 500,000 Bic pens that year. Mr. Biro died in 1987, age 86, having accumulated over 50 patents.

263

In 1947 Milton Reynolds had Bill Odum fly him around the world with a plane load of Reynolds ball point pens. He handed pens out wherever he went, that could "write under water". L.J. Biro, in Argentina, had the patent on them, later called "Bic".

Christopher Latham Sholes, 1819-1890.

Christopher Latham Sholes, a Milwaukee printer, patented the typewriter in 1867. Unable to find anyone to manufacture it, he dejectedly sold the rights to the typewriter to James Densmore of Meadowville, PA for $12,000 after he had made 25 or 30 improved models between 1867 and 1873. Densmore persuaded Philo Remington, then making guns and sewing machines, to make 1000 typewriters for him. Remington's first shipment of typewriters went out in 1874, but he had to take most of them back for adjustments. They sold less than 200 that first year.

In late 1874, Mark Twain saw a person demonstrate the new typewriter, the Remington No. 1, typing 57 words in a minute. Twain bought one on the spot. The price tag was $125, a lot of money in those days and an expensive gamble on an untried technology. He later found that the typist's 57 words a minute were the result of typing the same phrase over and over again. But Twain took the No. 1 home and wrote a letter to his brother: "I AM TRYING TO GET THE HAND OF THIS NEW F/FANGLED WRITING MACHINE, BUT IT PILES AN AWFUL LOT OF WORDS ON ONE PAGE." Twain would soon master his machine sufficiently to become what may be the first author to submit a typed manuscript, possibly Tom Sawyer, to a publisher, published in 1876.

Mark Twain bought one of Philo Remington's first typewriters in 1874, patented by Latham Sholes in 1867, to type the first printed manuscript titled "Tom Sawyer".

Thirteen years later, in 1886, the Remington Arms Company sold the unprofitable typewriter division back to Densmore, who still had faith in Shole's typewriter. Sales started climbing in the 1890s as other manufacturers entered the market, when Shole's patents ran out. Finally, in 1899 the Assistant Secretary of the U.S. Treasury ordered all records be typewritten. This caused typing schools to spring up and by 1910 there were over two million lady typists in offices everywhere. Mr. Sholes died February 17, 1890, which was 10 years before his typewriter really took off in a big way. *Parts gleaned from Jake Page article 1-1-91 Smithsonian.*

264

When Sholes' patent ran out on the typewriter, other manufacturers started making them.

HAROLD WARP
PIONEER VILLAGE
Minden, Neb. 68959 FOUNDATION

While James Ritty, a cafe owner, watched a device count the revolutions of the propeller, on an 1878 cruise to Europe, he thought "why not make a machine like that to count coins". He did just that and invented the cash register in 1879. This "thief catching machine" was considered a "white elephant" for several years.

Cash registers were slow to be accepted.

"Be sure a thing is needed" Edison learned when his first invention, at age 15, a vote counter, didn't interest congressmen.

One day in 1878 during a cruise to Europe a midwestern cafe owner asked if he might visit the engine room of the ship. He was a stocky man with a handlebar mustache that swept elegantly across his face. As he watched the device that counted the turns of the ship's propeller an idea slowly began to take shape in his mind. "If the revolutions of a propeller could be counted automatically, why wouldn't it be possible to make a machine that would count the sales in a store – in his own cafe for example?" This chance observation made by James Ritty in 1878, amid the din of a ship's engine room, gave birth to the cash register – an invention that has influenced the lives of millions of people throughout the world. Today the cheerful jingle of the machines can be heard in over 100 countries. The ring of the cash register is perhaps the world's most familiar sound effect. The first register looked like a big wall clock with two hands that indicated dollars and cents. Like many other inventions, the machine ran into opposition at the time. Ritty invented the cash register in 1879. Jeered by his contemporaries, he sold the rights to his "thief-catching machine" for $1,000. The invention was generally regarded as a "white elephant" until it was purchased in 1884 by John H. Patterson, founder of the National Cash Register Company. Patterson bought the invention – and a small cash register factory – for $6,500 from a man named Phillips, but even Patterson was assailed by doubts as to whether he had made a good bargain. After making the purchase, he attempted to call off the deal and offered to let Phillips keep the $2,000 if the latter would take the machine back. "Take it back?" the seller is reported to have said, "I wouldn't take it back as a gift." Since that time, the company has manufactured more than 5,000,000 of the machines. Sales in 1958 were about $400 million.

265

HAROLD WARP
PIONEER VILLAGE
Minden, Neb. 68959 *FOUNDATION*

Thomas Edison's first major invention, at age 15, was a system for recording Congressional votes in the House and Senate, but congressmen, he learned, would not buy a machine to replace their votes. "Be sure a thing is needed, then go ahead" was a lesson he learned the hard way. 266

A 30 ton monster, requiring 15,000 square feet of floor space, powered by 18,000 vacuum tubes, housed in a set of frames and chassis built by a local kitchen cabinet maker, spit out the first computerized answer in February 1946. The computer was built by two professors at the Moore Electrical Engineering School in Philadelphia, Pennsylvania; 38 year old Dr. Mauchly and 26 year old Dr. Eckert.

The first computer (1946) filled this school room.

The U.S. Government had authorized $62,000 to build the "ENIAC" (Electronic Numerical Integrator and Calculator), but it finally cost over $400,000 and came too late to compute the balistic firing tables it was designed to do during World War II. In 1947, patent #3,120,606 was issued to John W. Mauchly and J. Presper Eckert.

In 1937, John V. Atanasoff, physics professor at Ames Iowa State College, conceived the idea of a computer, using radio vacuum tubes, on his way home from the lab. With the help of Clifford E. Bennett, one of his students, they commenced work on it in 1939. Dr. Atanosoff had difficulty in raising money to continue his work on his Atanasoff Bennett Computer (ABC). By 1941, when he had it operational, at a cost of $60,000, he was unable to raise the money to produce his "ABC". When World War II came on Bennett took a draft deferred position and Atanasoff joined the U.S. Naval Ordinance Lab. He never got around to patent his "ABC" (Atanasoff Bennett Computer). During the time that Dr. Atanasoff was trying to get financial support, he contacted John Mauchly, his fellow scientist and explained his "ABC" to him.

They were not the real creators of the computer.

John V. Atansoff

Judge Larson discovered in 1973 that the first computer "ENIAC", built by Mauchly and Eckert, patented by them in 1947, costing the U.S. government $40,000, was a copy of the "ABC" stolen from Dr. Atanasoff in 1941.

Mr. Mauchly visited Dr. Atanasoff at his home for the better part of a week in June 1941, during which time the "ABC" was demonstrated to Mauchly. Four years later, the "ENIAC", built and patented by Mauchly & Eckert realized Atanasoff's vision of his ABC computer. In 1967, Sperry Rand, who then owned the "ENIAC" patents, sued Honeywell for not paying computer royalties. Honeywell's lawyers came across a mention of Atanasoff, tracked him down and proved in court that he was privy to ENIAC patents, from information Mauchly had gained from Atanasoff when he spent nearly a week in Atanasoff's home in the early 1940s. As a result, in October 19, 1973, Judge Larson, of U.S. District Court in Minneapolis, ruled ENIAC patents invalid, as "having derived subject matter from Dr. John Vincent Atanasoff." 267

HAROLD WARP PIONEER VILLAGE FOUNDATION
Minden, Neb. 68959

Chester Carlson, on October 22, 1938, in a second floor kitchen, behind a beauty parlor in Astoria, New York, after four years of experimenting, trying to make dry copies with static electricity finally succeeded. He pressed a piece of waxed paper to a sulphur coated aluminum plate and when he pulled it away, it had made a copy of the day's date. That night xerography (from the Greek, meaning dry writing) had been born "xerox". Carlson, who worked in the patent department of an electronics firm, had graduated from law school in 1935, by going to night classes. That night, in 1938, he and his helper went out to celebrate, but they were 15 years too early. Eastman Kodak, IBM and others had their own copying machines and were not interested. "I almost gave up a few times, but I couldn't let it rest," Carlson said, and finally, in 1944 he made a deal with the non-profit "Battelle Memorial Institute" of Columbus, Ohio to develop his xerography for 75% of the profits. They ran out of money and Carlson scratched together $15,000 from friends, relatives and his own savings, but they still couldn't sell their machine that made copies from static electricity. Finally, the Haloid Company (forerunner of Xerox) bought commercial rights in 1947 and Carlson quit his job when he got his first royalty check for $2500. But again the jubilation was premature and Carlson went back to his desk at his old job. After years of experimenting and sales resistance their efforts finally paid off. With the advent of the Xerox 914 Copier in 1960 Carlson got his reward. It was staggering. By 1965 his royalties had reached $20 million, but he still liked to putter in his workshop and drop in at the Xerox labs once a week. When he died in 1965, age 62, Xerox was an $800 million a year firm and Carlson's fortune was $150 million. 268

After Chester Carlson had worked on a static electricity copier "in his second floor kitchen for four years", he finally succeeded October 22, 1938. But he ran out of money trying to sell his "Xerox" electrostatic copier for the next 15 years.

When Marvin Camras, 22 year old son of a Russian immigrant, living in Chicago south side, came up with the idea of a magnetic tape recorder, he was not concerned with its implications. He said "My cousin Bill Korzan wanted to hear his own voice and I was familiar with the fact that Valdemar Poulsen, Danish scientist, had recorded voice between magnets in the 1890s. We drilled holes through an electromagnet and fed the wire through them. We did it for the fun of it. I was as surprised as anyone when his voice did come out." Camras showed his machine to the professors at Illinois Institute of Technology in 1938. They suggested he take it to the Armour Institute of Technology for patenting and marketing. He did just that and stayed with them for 42 years, continuing to turn out inventions. By 1977, he had been awarded over 500 patents that the ITT says built their $15 million research tower at Chicago's 35th and State Street. It was truly a "sound" invention. 269

When Marvin Camra was 22 years old, he said, "my cousin wanted to hear his own voice (so) we drilled a hole through an electro-magnet, fed a wire through and I was surprised when his voice came out". Thus the tape recorder was born in 1938.

HAROLD WARP
PIONEER VILLAGE
Minden, Neb. 68959 FOUNDATION

Bolton Sullivan
(Son of Joe Sullivan)
Ed Michael's first "Skilsaw", in 1921, was a tiny rotary saw blade attached to a malted milk mixer, for cutting sugar cane.

A malted milk mixer became the first skilsaw. In 1923 an article appeared in a New Orleans newspaper, stating a new rotary blade machete for cutting sugar cane had been invented by one Edmund Michael. The article was read by a former Minneapolis real estate salesman, Joseph Sullivan, on the train, while en route to the Florida land boom of the early 1920s. Salesman Sullivan reversed his direction and went back to New Orleans, looked up Michael and inspected his rotary machete. It consisted of a tiny rotary saw blade attached to the tip of a machette, crudely powered by a malted milk mixer motor. Sullivan told Michael that if he would make a sturdier model, capable of sawing wood, he might be interested. Michael did that and contacted Sullivan again. While they were eating supper one evening Michael decided to name it "Skilsaw" and the two men came to an agreement to set up shop in Chicago. That little mixmaster motored machete that Michael invented in 1921 hatched quite a family of handy electric tools. 270

500 Fascinating Facts

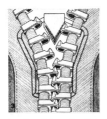

Judson's "zipper" almost floundered before it found its way into tobacco pouches.

The zipper was patented in 1891 by Witcomb L. Judson, a mechanical engineer, primarily to replace shoe buttons and shoe laces. Judson and a Chicago attorney set up the Universal Fastener Company to mass produce them. The early zippers had a tendency to open when they should not, and did not prove practical for shoes, but found their way into tobacco pouch closures instead. The company was saved from bankruptcy by a Swedish engineer, Gideon Sunback, who refined the zipper so it did not have the embarrassing habit of opening when it shouldn't. They were made of rust-proof metals until in the 1950s when plastic zippers became common. 271

He copied a cocklebur.

While picking cockleburs off after a hunting trip, George deMestro got the idea to develop "Velcro" fasteners, that he introduced in 1958.

One day in the late 1940s, Swiss inventor George deMestral brushed up against some cockleburs while hunting in the Jura Mountains. Plucking the pesky prickers from his clothes, deMestral marvelled at their tenacious grip. He discovered the source of their strength later when he examined a burr under a microscope. He saw that it was a collection of slender hooks that dug right in to a mat of fabric or fur. This natural phenomenon inspired the two portions of the "Velcro" fastening system introduced in 1958. One piece is covered with tiny, cocklebur-type hooks of nylon monofilament, and its mate is covered with woven, round-topped loops of a nylon multifilament. "Velcro" fasteners are used to secure and close shoes, blood pressure cuffs, interior auto trim, caps, breakaway clothing, wallets, wrist and ankle weights, camera bags, etc., etc. 272

Original map of the Americas.

Did you know that California was listed on an original map of North and South America in 1721 as an island? At the Harold Warp Pioneer Village at Minden in south central Nebraska, you can see this map in the art department; also other early maps of America that are surprisingly accurate in spite of the crude charting equipment used at that time. 273

Glass coins

Glass coins of varying colors were used in Egypt from 908 to 1171 A.D. Each denomination was a different color and were exchangeable for gold on demand.   274

Origin of "two bits".

The Spanish dollar, used by several of the U.S. Colonies, and later by the U.S. Government, consisted of eight Reals, each worth 12½¢, commonly called a "bit". As this Spanish money circulated freely in the U.S. until 1857 with official sanction, the quarter dollar came to be known as two bits.   275

Origin of "pin money".

In 1776-78 the newly formed Continental Congress issued notes printed on cardboard. These notes broke easily when folded. The pieces were pinned together when they got separated. Thus it became known as "pin money".   276

Fractional currency

Postage stamps were used for money during the Civil War.

When coins disappeared from circulation during the Civil War, people commenced using postage stamps for legal tender. In 1862, Congress authorized the printing of the first 25¢ stamps in clusters, with Washington's picture on them, to be used for money. The second printing was authorized by Congress in 1863, to print unperforated stamps in denominations of 5¢, 10¢, 25¢, and 50¢, all described on the face as "Postage Currency". Several printings followed. Over $15,000.00 of this fractional currency printed by the U.S. Government between 1862 and 1876 was never redeemed.   277

Masai men still trade cattle for wives.

The wealth of primitive people consisted largely of flocks and herds, as is shown in our term *pecuniary*, which harks back to a Latin word for cattle. The Masai tribes of East Africa still use cattle for barter and exchange, especially to obtain wives.   278

How the "Dollar" got its name.

The name American "dollar" came into being by way of Austro-Germany and Spain. In 1520 Count Stephen Schlik minted silver coins in Bohemia's Joachimsthal; it was called Joachimsthaler groschen. It became popularly known as thaler and pronounced taaler – or dollar. Spanish coins minted in Mexico and Peru resembled the thaler and showed two pillars to symbolize the Straits of Gibralter; later the two pillars or bars were superimposed on the S giving us the $ sign. The newly independent American colonies gave the federal government the exclusive right to coin money. The first American silver dollar was the Liberty Head issue of 1794.   279

William H. Jackson was known as "The Picture Maker of the West". He made the very first photographs of Yellowstone Park and Old Faithful Geyser, the ancient cliff dwellings in Colorado, Arizona and New Mexico. In making his pictures, albumen for carrying the silver nitrate was obtained from wild bird's eggs and light for printing his pictures was obtained from the sun. William H. Jackson was also a meticulous artist. When he painted a picture of horses on a stage coach, the correct number of spokes were shown on the wagon, as well as every piece of harness in its proper place. He lived to be 100 and did most of his painting after the age of 90. He died in 1942. Twenty-seven of Jackson's original paintings can be seen at the Harold Warp Pioneer Village, as well as his paint box, brushes and also the equipment he used to photograph Yellowstone Park. His picture "A Remount Station" is a painting of a Western Nebraska Pony Express Station which is now at Harold Warp's Pioneer Village, authentically furnished, with a three horse barn out back.   280

Picture maker of the old west.

Wm. H. Jackson used wild bird's eggs for making first pictures of Yellowstone Park.

Pony Express station painted by Jackson is now at Pioneer Village.

Very few of John Rogers' groups still exist, for they were made of clay, but Warp's Pioneer Village has 76 on display.

Rogers' Groups of Statuary were very popular between 1860 and 1910. For over 30 years (1859 to 1893) John Rogers, in his small new Canaan, Connecticut studio, successfully portrayed the true likeness of the American scene, such as the farm, the village store, school, church and social life of the people. His statuary was cast in clay, therefore they were inexpensive, but very fragile and few remain in existence today. He produced 80 Rogers' groups between 1859 and 1893, priced at $10 to $20. Fortunately Harold Warp was able to find 76 different John Rogers' Groups over a period of 40 years and these are now on display at his Pioneer Village at Minden, Nebraska in humidity controlled, airtight glass cases.   281

Some of John Rogers' 80 groups, 1859-1893.

In 1247 A.D. the Chinese discovered how to make black powder, as reported by Mr. Bacon. It consisted of a simple mixture of 75% saltpeter, 15% charcoal and 10% sulphur.   282

Black powder is nothing but charcoal, sulphur and saltpeter.

"Dumdum" bullets were first made in Dumdum, India.

Dumdum bullets originated in India in the 19th century, when British troops found that their bullets penetrated but did not halt their foe. So they had hollow nose bullets produced in the city of Dumdum, near Calcutta, India. Some troops made their own "Dumdum" bullets thereafter by cutting off the tip to make it blunt, then cutting a deep cross in the exposed soft lead, so it would expand on contact, to produce "stopping power".   283

Eli Whitney

Eli Whitney, inventor of the cotton gin, should be really called the father of mass production. Contracting with the U.S. Government to make 10,000 muskets with interchangeable parts taking 11 years, he started mass production ideas in 1789. The lathe Eli Whitney used is on display at the Harold Warp Pioneer Village in Minden, in south central Nebraska.   284

Samuel Colt 1814-1862

He didn't live to see metal cartridges used in his firearms.

Samuel Colt was a circus performer who patented his "ratchet acting locking revolving cylinder firearm" in 1835 when he was 20 years old. He died a millionaire in 1862, age 48, nine years before his Colt firearm was converted from percussion to metallic cartridge in 1871. He didn't live to see the Colt "Peacemaker" revolver and the Colt "6 Shooter Carbine" rifle, both using 44 caliber cartridges that helped to tame the West.   285

HAROLD WARP PIONEER VILLAGE FOUNDATION
Minden, Neb. 68959

Sharps buffalo rifle
SHARPS BUFFALO GUN
1869
"Almost Obliterated The Buffalo"

Sharpshooter – This word originated with the remarkable accuracy of Sharp's Buffalo Gun. Although only 2,000 of them were made between 1865 and 1874, they were responsible for annihilating 50 million bison on the Nebraska and Kansas plains, in a 10 year period. This gun, as well as the complete evolution of weapons, from spears to automatic rifles, can be seen at the Harold Warp Pioneer Village in south central Nebraska.   286

HAROLD WARP PIONEER VILLAGE FOUNDATION
Minden, Neb. 68959

Custer's 241 men with single shot guns were no match for the Sioux warriors on June 25, 1876. The Indians had Winchester 12 shot repeaters, purchased with their Black Hills Gold, before the government ordered them to move out. (See a Sioux rifle at the Pioneer Village)

Sioux Indian Carbine – 1876 – "caused Custer's last stand". The Sioux Indians, under leadership of Crazy Horse, wiped out Custer and his 241 men at the battle of the Little Big-Horn on June 25, 1876 with their raw-hide protected carbines, just like they had previously wrapped their bows with rawhide where they held them. These guns were bought by the Indians with Black Hills gold, discovered on their land in 1874. Custer's men were "sitting targets" armed with their single shot guns of Civil War vintage, against the Sioux who literally "mowed them down" with these new type twelve shot repeating Winchester carbines. Incidentally the Black Hills belonged to the Indians, by treaty, and they were fighting to protect what they rightfully owned. Their lands were being overrun by white men seeking gold.   287

HAROLD WARP PIONEER VILLAGE FOUNDATION
Minden, Neb. 68959

Daisy Air Rifle

"Why Clarence, it's a Daisy" said Lewis Hough when Clarence Hamilton showed him the wire stock BB gun he had designed as a free premium with his windmills in 1886.

In 1886 Clarence J. Hamilton was manufacturing windmills in Plymouth, Michigan. He designed a simple air gun that would shoot BBs, as a premium to sell his windmills. When they tried it, Vice President Lewis Hough was so pleased he said "Why Clarence, it's a Daisy." People preferred his "Daisy" air gun to his "Plymouth" windmills, so he started selling the single shot, wire stock Daisy for 50 cents. In 1958 the Daisy Air Rifle Company moved to Rogers, Arkansas, long after they quit selling windmills. One of these 50¢ Daisies with a wire stock can be seen at Warp's Pioneer Village. 288

In 1858 Marsh patented a harvester that carried grain by continuous belt to a table where two men stood on footboards and tied the oncoming grain into bundles. In 1878 the Appleby twine knotter was attached to the Marsh harvester to become the Deering Grain Binder. Wm. Deering had paid Appleby $80,000 for his knotter made originally from a cherry twig, but Appleby lost it all before he died. 289

Bill Deering paid Appleby $80,000 for the grain binder knotter he made from a cherry twig.

McCormick and Deering, rival manufacturers of grain reapers, fought bitterly from 1878, when Deering introduced the first twine binder, until 1902 when J.P. Morgan purchased both companies to start International Harvester Company. Their children later intermarried and now McCormick and Deering lie buried side by side in a Chicago cemetery with identical tombstones. 290

McCormick and Deering, bitter grain reaper rivals, lay buried side by side in Graceland Cemetery, Chicago.

The Case dealer emblem.

One of the oldest advertising symbols was the Case Company "Old Abe" eagle that lasted 104 years (1865 to 1969). "Old Abe" cast in iron three feet high that stood in front of every Case dealer's premises has become a collector's item. 291

One day in 1873 Isaac Elwood found Glidden cranking out barbed wire in his farmyard with a coffee grinder and a grindstone. Elwood covinced Glidden to patent his "barbed wire" and bought half interest for $265.

Isaac Ellwood

Bet-A-Million Gates

In late 1874 Glidden sold out for $60,000. John Gates, a West Chicago hardware dealer, sold his store and went to Texas to sell ranchers barbed wire, by then being made with a steam engine in Dekalb, Ill.

One day in the summer of 1873, Isaac Ellwood and his wife drove to the Glidden farm, near DeKalb, Illinois, where they found Glidden industriously turning the crank of an old coffee grinder. From the coffee grinder were dropping wire barbs. Then Glidden slid the barbs onto a sixteen-foot length of greased wire, spacing them and clamping them tight. Proudly, he showed Isaac Ellwood how he had rigged the coffee grinder into a barbed-wire producer and then he took his visitors to a grindstone he had converted into a twister. He fastened two strands of wire, one barbed, the other unbarbed, to a tree, tied the other ends to the grindstone and then he turned the handle to twist the strands tightly together. These double strands, said he, not only would keep the barbs in place, but would keep the fence taut. "You've got the answer!" shouted Ellwood, "Let's talk business."

Glidden sold Ellwood half interest in his invention for $265. Ellwood would supply the wire, arrange for a factory in DeKalb, and handle the sales. Glidden secured his patent in October 1873, and in six months Ellwood organized a company with a factory on DeKalb's Main Street. Six boys were hired to climb trees around the building. They hauled up lengths of wire which were stretched from the trees to the ground and they happily worked ten hours a day stringing the barbs which were later clamped into place by older workmen. Sales boomed, especially in the Illinois territory. Ellwood's increased orders for wire stimulated the curiosity of Charles G. Washburn and Philip W. Moen, the country's largest wiremakers at Worcester, Massachusetts. Washburn hurried to DeKalb and what he saw instantly inspired him to buy the Ellwood-Glidden plant. Ellwood refused to sell, but Glidden sold them his interests late in 1874 for $60,000 and lifetime royalties.

Twenty-one-year-old hardware merchant, John W. Gates, at Turner's Corner (now West Chicago), Illinois, became so interested that he sold his hardware store at the corner of Main and Galena Streets for $700 and took a job with Col. Isaac Ellwood at $30 per month for expenses, to sell barbed wire to ranchers in Texas. By then a steam engine had replaced the coffee grinder for making

Judge Gary

By 1880 barbed wire had dropped to $150 per mile; Elwood had contracts to fence 59 railroad rights of way and Gates and Gray had organized the "Infringers Combine" to make their own barbed wire.

Andrew Carnegie

In 1886 Gates bought 50,000 tons of steel in England for $10 a ton, sold Carnegie 10,000 tons at an inflated price and decided to set up "Consolidated Steel and Wire Co." to control the market.

barbed wire at DeKalb. John Gates took a train to San Antonio, Texas, where he staged a rodeo in a barbed wire enclosure, to prove it could keep in Texas longhorns. He sold barbed wire at $400 per mile, for replacing cowboys, to ranchers who came to see his rodeo. John W. Gates was on his way to undreamed of wealth. Infringers were springing up by the dozens, making many different kinds of barbed wire. Isaac Ellwood picked out one of the infringers, "Haish", and sued him. All infringers joined in the defense and although Ellwood won the first court decision in 1880, which would have netted him $3 million a year in royalties from these barbed wire infringers, they appealed. Ellwood's star salesman, John Gates, on advice of attorney Elbert H. Gary, his boyhood swimming pal from Winfield, decided to organize the "Infringers Combine". He was then 28, the price of barbed wire had dropped to $150 per mile and that year his old boss, Isaac Ellwood, had received contracts from 59 railroad companies to fence their right of ways. Ellwood, by then, had his own source of iron, under the name of Ellwood, Washburn, Moen, and so did Gates by consolidating the infringers, operating as the Southern Wire Company in St. Louis.

These Barbed Wire battlers were using so much steel that they caught the eye of steel czar, Andrew Carnegie, and railroad tycoon, Jay Gould, when they bought up several small steel mills in Pennsylvania. In 1886 John Gates went to New York and contacted J. Pierpont Morgan, the money baron of Wall Street. Morgan sent him to England where Gates bought up 50,000 tons of steel at ten dollars per ton, sending the price of steel up and creating such a shortage that Carnegie actually bought 10,000 tons of it at inflated prices. When Gates saw how easy it was to make money on steel he thought it was foolish for the wire fence makers to fight among themselves, so in December 1892 he succeeded in getting the prominent ones into one combination as the "Consolidated Steel and Wire Company", with a capitalization of $4 million much more than the actual physical value of the combined properties. This Combine, in addition to controlling the price and output of barbed, and twisted wire, also controlled wire staples, tacks,

J. Pierpont Morgan

When J.P. Morgan discovered what barbed wire had built up, he bought them all out, created and capitalized the "U.S. Steel Co." for $1,404,000,000.

The use of "Bob Wire" as it was commonly called, increased tremendously as the years went by.

Year	Tons	Miles	Year	Tons	Miles
1874	5	10	1880	40,000	80,000
1875	300	600	1881	60,000	120,000
1876	1,500	3,000	1882	80,000	160,000
1877	7,000	14,000	1883	100,000	200,000
1878	13,000	26,000	1884	125,000	250,000
1879	25,000	50,000	1885	130,000	260,000

Elwood and Gates bought Quail hunting ground in Texas, drilled an oil well that blew in January 10, 1901, to become "Texas Oil Co.".

nails, plain wire and rod stock. In 1893 they started grinding up the klinker and slag in their steel mills and selling it as "Portland" cement, that a man by the name of Whiting had patented. By 1896 the coffee grinder barbed wire venture had blossomed out to twelve blast furnaces, four Bessemer steel plants, an open hearth plant, two rail mills, a billet mill, two rod mills and a plate mill, controlling interest in two railroad companies, a cement plant and the entire wire staple and nail industry.

In 1898, J.P. Morgan, who had quietly gained control of Consolidated Steel Company, replaced John Gates as chairman with Elbert H. Gary, John's old boyhood swimming pal from Winfield, Illinois. Morgan proceeded to gobble up several iron companies, including John D. Rockefeller's vast iron ore deposits in northern Minnesota, as well as the Illinois, Joliet, and Eastern railroad. He had Judge Gary vastly overcapitalize the analgamation at $56 million as the Federal Steel Company. Gates and Ellwood continued to run their highly successful American Steel and Wire Company until 1901 when the U.S. Steel Company was put together at a stock value of $1,404,000,000, with an actual value of somewhere around $300 million. Its creator, banker J. Pierpont Morgan.

Andrew Carnegie pocketed $492 million in the deal and devoted the rest of his life to charitable and educational enterprises. Ellwood and Gates both bought quail hunting grounds on Lake Sabine, Texas and each built $50,000 hunting lodges at the end of the railroad, which they also owned by the time it was completed in 1900. A dock and hotel were built, taking Mr. Stillwell's first name "Port Arthur". One Patillo Higgins, who was drilling for oil twenty miles from Port Arthur ran out of money. Gates reorganized the venture, taking 46% of the stock for himself and 8% went to a close friend, Craig Cullinan. Jointly they owned 52% and started drilling again. Gates called it "The Texas Oil Company" (Texaco). On January 10, 1901 the well blew in. It was "Old Spindletop". The oil squirted 160 feet in the air, ruining completely the quail hunting grounds of John "Bet-a-Million" Gates and Col. Isaac Ellwood. Gates died on a trip to England August 9, 1911, leaving an estate of $50 million. The

Charles Martin Hall, working with homemade equipment in the family woodshed, discovered a low-cost process for separating aluminum from its oxide and thus started America's gigantic aluminum industry.

Ellwood heirs still live in DeKalb but Gates' only son, Charles, died an alcoholic two years after his dad in 1913, and John's wife, Dellora, died in 1918, leaving $38 million to her brother, Col. Ed Baker, who endowed St. Charles, Illinois with many projects from his brother-in-law's huge fortune. Baker died in 1959, at the age of 90, leaving over $17 million of John "Beta-a-Million" Gates' huge fortune still intact to his niece. Who could ever have guessed that Mr. Glidden's coffee grinder would grind out not only the U.S. Steel Company but also "Texaco" Oil Company.   292

Minden, Neb. 68959

From a backyard woodshed the mighty aluminum industry developed. On February 23, 1886 Charles Martin Hall, a 22-year-old minister's son, learned how to extract aluminum from clay (bauxite) in his father's woodshed in Oberlin, Ohio. On Thanksgiving Day 1888, Hall produced his first pound of aluminum with the help of Arthur V. Davis, another preacher's son from Boston, who kept the fires going all the night before, 2½ years after Hunt discovered the process. The equipment for producing the first aluminum was financed by Alfred B. Hunt, a 33-year-old metallurgist of the Pittsburgh testing laboratories. He saw the possibility of producing aluminum from common clay, and put up $20,000.00 of his own money to purchase the required equipment that was set up in a small pilot plant on Smallman Street in Pittsburgh, PA. By the fall of 1889 (one year later) production had gradually increased to 50 pounds of aluminum per day at $1 to $2 per pound, with Hunt and Davis taking cat naps at the plant to keep the furnaces going day and night, but they ran out of money. Hunt contacted the local bankers, 38-year-old Andrew Mellon and his brother Michael for $4000 to cover an overdue loan they could not pay in January 1890. Andrew Mellon told Hunt to come back next day, which he did. That January afternoon the Mellons inspected the facilities of the "Pittsburgh Reduction Company". The next morning Andrew Mellon told Hunt, Davis and Hall that they needed considerably more than $4000. Andrew Mellon agreed

Captain Alfred E. Hunt, a leading metallurgist of the Eighties, foresaw a great aluminum industry based on the Hall process, and became first president of The Pittsburgh Reduction Company.

Andrew Mellon

In January 1890 Hunt, Hall and Davis ran out of money, so Andrew Mellon came to their rescue with $4000, but told them they needed much more. He and his brother Michael acquired 60 shares at $6000 per share that really put ALCOA on the map.

Although Charles Hunt was a minister's son, he willed that none of his $30 million be used for instruction in theology.

to acquire 60 shares of stock at $6000 per share if they would move the plant to a four acre tract at a bend in the Allegheny River at Kensington, PA, which they did. By 1893, (three years later), larger facilities were needed and as it took lots of electricity to make aluminum, it was decided to relocate at Niagara Falls, to take advantage of hydro-electric power, again financed by Mellon Bank. This huge aluminum plant went into production August 26, 1895. Alcoa remained the only aluminum producer until World War II, when the U.S. Government set up other producers.   293

HAROLD WARP
PIONEER VILLAGE
Minden, Neb. 68959 FOUNDATION

What happened to the men who started "Alcoa"? Charles Hall remained an inventor until his death in 1914, age 50, leaving $30 million to various colleges, with the understanding that none of it would be used for instruction in theology, although he was a minister's son and a religious man himself. Arthur Vining Davis became the guiding genius of Alcoa in 1899 and remained its largest stockholder for the next 50 years. During World War II the U.S. Government set up competitors to Alcoa, that had been the sole producer of aluminum. January 16, 1951, Arthur Vining Davis was ordered by the U.S. Supreme Court to divest himself of his "Alcoa" stock. He proceeded to convert his stock into Florida real estate until he owned 1/8 of Dade County (Miami) and 1/5 of Broward County (Ft. Lauderdale) under the "Arvida" name, ARthur VIning DAvis and "Velda Farms" using parts of his name and parts of his wife Elizabeth's name. When he died November 17, 1962, aged 95, his barber sued his estate for two years on back barber bills he had forgotten to pay. Andrew Mellon, before he died in 1937, age 85, set aside $15 million to build the "Mellon Art Institute" in the mall in Washington, D.C. and stocked it with 132 paintings for which he had paid $47 million. He also set up an $8 million endowment for their upkeep. In a joint session, Congress exonerated ex-Secretary of the U.S. Treasury Andrew Mellon of millions of dollars in tax evasion three months after his death.   294

Arthur Vining Davis

When ordered to divest himself of his "ALCOA" stock, he bought up 1/8 of Dade County and 1/5 of Broward County in Florida (Miami and Ft. Lauderdale).

Arthur Vining Davis, Alcoa's honorary chairman and the last of the pioneer group that started Alcoa, died on Nov. 17, 1962, at the age of 95. He was the company's first employee and helped to pour the first commercial aluminum ingot on Thanksgiving Day in 1888.

Little is known about how the aluminum industry grew, because there was only one producer for over 60 years, "Alcoa" (Aluminum Company of America), headed by one man, Arthur Vining Davis. He became the guiding genius in 1899 and remained so until ordered to divest himself of his Alcoa stock, in a U.S. Supreme Court ruling January 16, 1951. He then commenced converting his "Alcoa" stock into Florida real estate until "ARVIDA" (ARthur VIning DAvis) owned 1/8 of Dade County (Miami) and 1/5 of Broward County (Ft. Lauderdale). He also raised and sold farm produce and ice cream under the name "VELDA", using parts of his and his wife Elizabeth's names.

295

HAROLD WARP
PIONEER VILLAGE
Minden, Neb. 68959 FOUNDATION

BIRTH OF THE JEEP – In 1938, Roy Evans, who then owned the American Bantam Car Company of Butler, PA, successor to the American Austin Company, loaned a few of their Bantam roadsters to the Pennsylvania National Guard for their summer maneuvers. The Guards praised them highly, except they had no 4 wheel drive.

The Bantams had originally been designed for use in movies and became the darlings of the Hollywood movie people, such as W.C. Fields, Buster Keaton and Will Rogers.

This was the prototype "Bantam" Carl Probst and Crist drove to Maryland 9/23/40 for testing.

In the summer of 1940 the U.S. Army decided they wanted a 4 wheel drive field car patterned after the Bantam and sent a prospectus out to all car manufacturers, calling for delivery in 49 days. Bantam won the contract to build what would become Jeep #1, to be completed by September 21, 1940. (The name "Jeep" derived later, when Ford was given a contract to make them for the U.S. Government under the code name "GPW" for General Purpose Willys). Bantam President Frank Fenn, and Harold Christ, factory manager, rounded up some of their old employees and contacted well known Detroit free-lance engineer, Karl Probst, who agreed to come to Butler and help turn out the car they promised to make a prototype of, for the U.S. Government. This they did. Karl Probst and

When "JEEP" orders were placed in November 1941, Bantam was ignored in favor of Willys and Ford.

Harold Crist personally drove Jeep #1 (not yet named) to Camp Holabird, Maryland, near Baltimore on Monday, September 23, 1940, for testing. The experienced army drivers reported that they had never received a test vehicle that performed as well as the Bantam.

The U.S. Govt. claimed the project was not patentable, but a competitive design. Apparently wary of Bantam's shaky financial position, coupled with the urgency of the European War, the army men allowed Ford and Willys-Overland to photograph, measure and draw up plans of Bantam's Jeep #1. In November 1941, the U.S. Government's evaluation eliminated the Bantam 40 BRC, claimed it was underpowered and the status of the company and its ability to mass produce were factors in their elimination. Bantams demise came in 1954, when their #1 Jeep jigs and dies were destroyed, and the fact that Bantam produced the first Jeep is not generally known today.

During World War II Willys made 361,349 "MB" (Jeeps) and Ford made 277,896 "GPW" (General Purpose Willys) Jeeps, thus the "GP" became "JEEP". At war's end thousands were dumped in the Pacific Ocean.

When the war started December 7, 1941, the name for jeeps became critical and by war's end, Willys had made 361,349 "MB" Jeeps and Ford had made 277,896 "GPW" jeeps. The way to tell them apart: Ford's "GPW" (General Purpose Willys) had an inverted "U" crossmember and the Willys "MB" had a tubular crossmember. It was believed Ford's "General Purpose" G-P evolved into the word "Jeep".

When World War II ended, thousands of Jeeps were dumped in the Pacific Ocean, rather than bring them back to the United States. As war surplus, some found their way into farmer's hands and some were purchased by gasoline service stations for snow removal and car towing. Their 4 wheel drive and front end winch were ideal for these purposes. Jeeps were made under the direction of Joseph W. Frazer, who resigned in 1944 and joined up with Henry Kaiser in 1946. They proceeded to make the Kaiser and Frazer cars at Willow-Run in Wayne, Michigan. Kaiser took over Willys-Overland in 1953, thus reacquiring the post-war 6 cylinder Jeepster that Willys introduced in 1948. Gleaned from L.M. "Pete" Rodgers article in 9-10-91 Antique Auto Magazine. 296

After World War II Willys introduced a 6 cylinder civilian Jeep in 1948, to be taken over by Kaiser in 1953.

500 Fascinating Facts

IHC's 1908 "Kerosene Annie" didn't sell but the 1915 "Waterloo Boy" did.

Introduced in 1908 by International Harvester Co., a tractor called "Kerosene Annie" was not accepted by the farmers because they preferred horses. It wasn't until 1915 when World War I drove farm prices up that the Waterloo Boy Model "N" was purchased in quantity. (Forerunner of John Deere tractors). By 1918 more than 8000 had been sold for pulling two bottom plows.   297

Ford Tractor Co.
Minneapolis, Minn.

Before Henry Ford introduced his tractor a Minneapolis made "FORD" appeared. For that reason Henry named his tractor "Fordson".

Henry Ford made no public announcement before introducing his Fordson tractor in 1917. A group of Minneapolis promoters had hired a young man named Ford and brought out "The Ford Tractor" ahead of Henry Ford, although it was not a success. This was why Ford named his tractor "Fordson."   298

Benjamin Holt and his dad had been building combines pulled by 32 horses since 1869 when they merged with C.L. Best, who had made steam powered crawler tractors since 1910, to form "Caterpillar Tractor Co." in 1925.

The Caterpillar Tractor Company, Peoria, Illinois was formed in 1925 with $12,300,000 by a merger of the C.L. Best Tractor Company of San Leandro, California, and the Holt Manufacturing Company which had plants at Stockton, California and Peoria, Illinois. Benjamin Holt was the organizer and holder of the "Caterpillar" trade mark. The Best Company was organized in 1910 and the Holt Company in 1892, a successor to earlier Holt firms dating back to 1869, when they made huge grain combines, pulled by 32 horses. Holt was not new at trying to make a tractor to replace all those horses for pulling a grain combine. Benjamin Holt tested the first steam operated crawler tractor on Thanksgiving Day in 1904. In 1906 he substituted a gasoline engine for steam. By 1908 Holt had built and sold eight track-type steam tractors and that year he took over his most bitter rival, Daniel Best. Two years later (in 1910) C.L. Best, son of Daniel Best, formed his own company to make "track-layers" in his father's old plant. Holt merged with this company 15 years later (in 1925) to form the "Caterpillar Tractor Co." In 1928 Caterpillar acquired the Russell Grader Manufacturing Company of Minneapolis, manufacturer of road-

Holt owned the "Caterpillar" trademark that he named his first crawler steam tractor in 1904.

110

Early tractors came in different forms.

building machines for more than 20 years. In 1931, a Diesel engine was introduced in the "Caterpillar". By then Ben Holt's horses were long gone, having been replaced with "horsepower". 299

The world's largest collection of antique farm tractors and trucks in running order is located in this little south central Nebraska town of Minden, at the Harold Warp Pioneer Village. 300

The first milking machine resembled a bolt cutter.

The first milking machine looked somewhat similar to a huge bolt cutter. It had similar handles that the milkman or milkmaid would pump with rubber cups over the cows teats, invented in 1860 by L.O. Colvin, New York. It created a suction as it was pumped. The second version had pedals like a bicycle, that the milker or milkmaid would sit on and crank with their feet to create a suction in the cups on the cows teats, patented in 1908 by Mr. Mehring. The third version was a hand pump that sucked the air out of an eight gallon milk can, which created a suction on cups that would be slipped over the cow's teats, patented in 1930. 301

The foot powered milker. It peddaled like a bicycle.

The hand pump created a vacuum in the milk can.

Lighting the home from the 1890s to 1915 was a complicated engineering feat that utilized a carbide light generator. Fifty pounds of carbide added to 50 pounds of water in an ingenious tank within a tank developed a gas that was piped to the house. Only the wealthy could afford this lighting system which can be seen in the evolution of lighting at the Harold War Pioneer Village at Minden in south central Nebraska. 302

The 1890 carbide (gas) light generators were usually outdoors.

The oat hulls contained furfural that prevented cannibalism.

During the 1930s nearly every farmer purchased an Oat Huller powered by a gasoline engine to remove the hulls before feeding oats to livestock, primarily chicks and pigs. In 1940 it was learned that furfural contained in the oat hulls was what prevented cannibalism among chicks and pigs. For this reason most farmers then discontinued the hulling of oats before feeding to livestock. 303

During that period when chick cannibalism was rampant, a patent, #547-683, was granted to Harold Warp for a red colored window material, to neutralize the color of blood inside the chicken coop and at the same time provide chicks with the sun's ultraviolet rays. He named it "Red Viotex". It had substantial sales for several years, being guaranteed to prevent cannibalism, during the years that it was not known the hulling of oats was the cause of cannibalism. 304

Warp's "RED VI-O-TEX" neut-
ralized the color of blood to
prevent chick cannibalism.

While going through a car wash one day in 1971, George Ballas of Houston, Texas noticed how the strings of the big cleaning brushes stood out straight when revolving at high speed. He wondered if this principle would work for trimming lawn edges. He punched holes in a tin can, strung pieces of nylon fish line through the holes and fastened it on his lawn mower in place of the blade. It worked, but he was turned down by over 20 distributors who didn't believe a nylon string could cut grass. Finally the Outdoor Equipment Company, a Houston distributor, gave him an order in 1972. Since then that nylon string (the Weed Eater) has cut quite a swath in lawns across the country. 305

The brushes in a 1971 car
wash gave George Ballas the
idea for his "Weed Whip".

Dr. John Kellogg couldn't be bothered with corn flakes.

Sylvester Graham
1794-1851

Perky's Shredded Wheat touched off the breakfast food boom in 1893.

Dr. John Kellogg, Seventh Day Adventist who ran a health sanitarium at Battle Creek, Michigan, was always concocting health foods for longevity of his patients in the 1870s, 80s and 90s. Among them he had many trade names such as "Avenola," "Nutola," "Granola," "Yogurt," "Peanut Butter," "Sanatas," "Vegetable Meat," etc., that he also sold by mail to his 1,200 sanitarium clients. He also had health drinks made from toasted grain, claimed easier on the nervous system than coffee, that he called "Caramel Cereal Coffee" and "Minute Brew."

In 1893 a Denver client, Mr. Henry D. Perky, brought a suitcase full of shredded wheat from Denver that he had made to relieve his own stomach distress. Perky had gotten the idea of making a milk covered cereal with the same ingredients "graham crackers" contained. Graham Crackers had been concocted by Sylvester Graham shortly before the Civil War to relieve stomach disorders. They are still being made today. Dr. Kellogg thought the shredded wheat biscuits would be a good health food. He asked Mr. Perky to make him a machine for shredding the cooked, dried wheat mush. On his way to Battle Creek with the "Shredded Wheat" machine for Dr. John Kellogg, Mr. Perky changed his mind and went on to Niagara Falls, where he started a factory himself, that still makes Shredded Wheat biscuits there. Beings Perky decided not to furnish Dr. John a machine, Kellogg decided that he would make a health food himself – similar to shredded wheat, so he had his wife roll out some cooked whole wheat dough with a rolling pin. He then dried and cracked it into pieces. This was in 1895. He claimed the idea came to him in a dream, (forgetting Perky and his shredded wheat, of course), and he called it "Flaked Breakfast Food". He then proceeded to feed it to his Kellogg Sanitarium patients and mail order customers. In 1894 Chas. W. Post, a former promoter, came to Dr. John Kellogg's sanitarium in a wheel chair to regain his health. He thought Dr. John had a good idea in his toasted cracked grain "Cereal Coffee" as a health drink. Post approached Dr. John to go together on a "Kellogg's Minute Brew". Dr. John would have no part of such a venture so

Chas. W. Post (1854-1914). His Postum and Grape Nuts preceded Kellogg's Corn Flakes by nearly a decade.

John Kellogg sold the stock his brother gave him in 1906, as he considered his younger brother "illiterate" and the stock worthless.

Post Toasties and Kelloggs became corn flakes competitors.

Post decided to go it alone on "Postum Cereal Food Coffee". He cooked up his first batch of Postum on January 1, 1895. He peddled his first batch from a handcart in Battle Creek. Post's venture was an immediate success. He later added "Grape Nuts" and "Elijah's Manna" with a biblical scene on the box. He changed the name to "Post Toasties" when he learned it was unlawful in England to commercialize the Bible. Grape Nuts and Postum made an ideal combination, for Post charred bran to make Postum, leaving the hulled wheat for making Grape Nuts, which he recommended for inflamed appendix, consumption, malaria, and loose teeth. By April 1895 his "Postum" sales had amounted to $856, by December $5,000. The next year they jumped to $265,000. He finally got to spending $1,000,000 a year in advertising and by 1903 Post's fortune had reached $10 million. He died in 1914, a multi-millionaire.

Dr. John had a younger brother, William K. Kellogg, whom he considered rather illiterate, that he put to work in 1880 running errands and doing odd jobs at six dollars a week plus board and room. In 1905, Chas. D. Bolin, a St. Louis insurance man that came to the sanitarium, seeing Post's success, propositioned Dr. John to form a corporation to make breakfast food. Dr. John Kellogg was not particularly interested but his (illiterate) brother, William K. Kellogg was, so Mr. Bolin and Wm. K. formed "The Toasted Corn Flakes Corporation" in 1906. William K. Kellogg was made president. At the time Wm. K. considered himself an old man of 46. Wm. K., in fairness to his brother, Dr. John, for havig developed the idea of health foods and drinks, had some stock issued in his brother John's name, and they printed a picture of Dr. John's sanitarium on the corn flakes box as a good will gesture. Dr. John Kellogg didn't think much of the stock and being a frugal man, gve it to some of his employees as a bonus in lieu of a salary increase before he departed on a trip to Europe. When Dr. John returned from Europe, he learned Wm. K. had used his life savings to buy up the stock Dr. John had given his employees before he departed for Europe. Furthermore, Wm. K. had placed on the box "The Genuine Bears This Signature – W.K.

500 Fascinating Facts

Wm. K. Kellogg took John's picture off the box in 1908.

20 million tons of borax was shoveled up and hauled out of Death Valley, California between 1883 and 1889. They made the 20 day, 165 mile trip to Harmony with 20 mule teams hitched to Mr. Harmon's 46,000 lb. wagon loads of borax.

A. Montgomery Ward

He came into Chicago in 1872 from Niles, Michigan, with $2400 and an idea to make the Post Office his salesman.

Kellogg". Dr. John didn't like this. Wm. K. Kellogg eventually paid a third million dollars to settle lawsuits with Dr. John Kellogg and the Michigan courts finally gave Wm. K. the exclusive right to the name "Kellogg's" on corn flakes boxes in 1920. The corn flakes business prospered. In 1908 Wm. K. took the picture of Dr. John's sanitarium off the corn flakes box and when Wm. K. died in 1951, aged 91, he had given away over fifty million dollars and had set up the "W.K. Kellogg Foundation", one of the largest foundations in the United States.   306

In 1881, a prospector recognized the "cottonballs" strewn across California's Death Valley as ulexite (a sodium calcium borate). Coleman soon bought up the Death Valley claims, plus another deposit to the southeast, and built the Harmony Borax Works there. Cottonball could be mined simply by shoveling it from the surface into sleds or wagons. But transportation was a much bigger problem. The nearest railroad was 165 miles away across dry, barren desert. So Coleman turned to wagons harnessed to 20-mule teams – thereby inspiring one of the U.S.'s longest-lived trademarks. His teams – actually usually 18 mules with two strong horses in the wheel positions – pulled two wooden wagons with a capacity of up to 46,000 lb. plus water, feed, and food for the two-man crew, making the grueling run from Mojave to Harmony and back in 20 days. During the heyday of the 20-mule teams from 1883 to 1889, they hauled 20 million lb. of borax out of Death Valley.   307

A. Montgomery Ward came to Chicago in 1872 from Niles, Michigan, with $2,400 and the idea of making the U.S. Post Office his salesman. Ward and his associate, George H. Thorne, rented a fourth-floor room at 825 North Clark Street and started the first mail order business in Chicago, in 1872, with an eight-page catalog. Inauguration of the Parcel Post System in 1912, coupled with the spread of rural free delivery, gave a big boost to the mail order business.   308

Richard W. Sears

He started selling watches by mail in Minnesota in 1886 and joined A.C. Roebuck in Chicago in 1893.

Alva C. Roebuck

His money gone, his last years were on Sears' payroll, shaking hands with customers, the writer among them, in 1946, at "Sears" Chicago store.

The great Chicago fire of 1871 sparked the first retail hardware store.

Richard Sears started selling watches by mail in Minnesota in 1886 when he was 23. He joined resources with A.C. Roebuck in Chicago in 1893 and that same year incorporated "Sears, Roebuck & Co.". In 1895 Julius Rosenwald purchased Roebuck's interest in the firm and Sears retired in 1908. The first Sears retail store was opened in 1925. Sears died in 1914 but Roebuck lived until 1948, making his living the last few years of his life by being on the payroll of Sears, Roebuck, going from store to store introducing himself to customers and shaking their hand. 309

Prior to the great Chicago Fire in 1871, Louis Stauber, who had learned the tinsmith trade in Switzerland, made pots, pans, and sundry items in his Chicago home, that he would take out on the streets to sell in a peddler's wagon. At that time most every type of cooking equipment was made by hand. After the great Chicago Fire in 1871, Louis Stauber received contracts from the government to make tin chimneys for temporary houses. This required additional space so he constructed a crude building beside his home for a shop. Folks had come to prefer Mr. Stauber's line of "Ace" pots and pans and sundry items, so in the building where he was making tin smoke stacks under contract he continued to carry his pots and pans on the shelves. When the government contracts were completed, Mr. Stauber had learned that folks would come to his place of business for quality merchandise, rather than he go to them. So he also put on his shelves kerosene lamps, charcoal irons, scrub boards, fly traps, tools, locks, etc., to help keep his family clothed and fed. From that humble beginning Ace Hardware Stores grew to a nationwide chain across the country, of which Louis Stauber's son, William, aged 68 in 1953, when interviewed, was vice-president and treasurer. William's sons entered the hardware business too, with one store in Chicago, another in Waukegan, Illinois. Thus the third generation carried on under the Stauber's Ace Hardware trade name that started before the days of the hardware store, with a peddler's wagon. 310

When F.W. Woolworth, a 21 year old farm boy, got a job in Watertown, New York's leading store for $10 per week, he convinced the owner to set up a 5¢ counter, which was an immediate success.

In 1875, F.W. Woolworth, a farmboy, took a job as stockroom boy, janitor, general handyman and relief clerk in the leading store in Watertown, New York at $10 a week. He was then 21. Noticing that several items were moving slowly, Woolworth persuaded one of the owners to group them together on a counter in the center of the store, where the purchaser could see and handle them. He called it the "5¢ counter" – the beginning of the original "5 & 10¢" store. This display of products met with instant approval. People came, saw, handled and bought – usually more than they intended to buy when they entered the store. Woolworth opened his first successful "5 & 10¢" store June 21, 1879, at Lancaster, Pennsylvania, after having failed with his first "Great Five Cent Store" and by 1886 Woolworth had seven stores in Pennsylvania, New York and New Jersey.　　　311

A devout, plain man, James Cash Penney became a legend in his lifetime. A man of simple, firm beliefs, he called his first store Golden Rule and ran all his stores on that principle. Born in Missouri in 1875, J.C. Penney was a minister's son, who was taught self-reliance early. When he was just eight years old, his father decided young James must buy his own clothes to learn the value of money. Later his father helped him get his first job with a merchant and asked him to teach his son the business. Young Mr. Penney opened his first store in Wyoming in 1902. In 1914, the company officially became the J.C. Penney Company and in 1975 was the biggest chain of department stores in the country, totaling 1700 units. J.C. Penney was legendary for his thriftiness and for his unusual memory; he rarely forgot a name, face, or encounter. His associates were astounded when, at over 80 years old, he remembered by name, and the store where he worked, an employee he had not seen since 1904. Mr. Penney once said he would rather be known as a Christian than as a millionaire. Prominently framed in his office was the motto on which he built his fortune: "Do unto others as you would have them do unto you." He lived (and visited his stores) until he was almost 100.　　　312

J.C. Penney

J.C. Penney was born in Missouri in 1875. When 8 years old his minister father told him to earn his own clothes, to teach himself reliance. As a result J.C. Penney opened his first "Golden Rule" store in Wyoming in 1902 at age 27.

John Wannemaker almost went bankrupt before his "fixed price" was adopted by other merchants.

Modern retailing began with John Wanamaker, a Philadelphia dry goods merchant. When he started in business, prices were not shown to the customer. The price was whatever the sales person could get. The problem was getting sales clerks who could outsmart Philadelphia's sharp housewives. In 1865 he hit on a novel idea. Why not offer everyone a fixed price marked on a large display stand? Wanamaker almost went bankrupt before the idea caught on. When it finally did, public approval forced other merchants to adopt the same practice. Thus began the fixed price. Priced but not packaged.   313

HAROLD WARP
PIONEER VILLAGE
Minden, Neb. 68959 FOUNDATION

He didn't always sell Levis. A Bavarian immigrant, he first sold Irish linen from a horse-drawn wagon in New York City alleys.

The Levi trademark.

In 1872 "Levi" Strauss, a 20-year-old Bavarian immigrant who was selling Belgian lace and Irish linen from a horse-drawn wagon in New York, received a letter from one of his customers, Jacob Davis in California. Davis asked Levi Strauss to consider entering a partnership to manufacture and sell a new kind of work pants he had developed to withstand the hardest kind of wear and conditions. The pants were not only made of heavy duck cloth but were also copper-riveted at key stress points and on pocket corners. Levi liked the samples Davis had sent him. A deal was struck and Strauss headed for San Francisco. They named the rugged pants "Levis". He never dreamed he would strike the Mother Lode with a product that would one day be known around the world. Its brand name is recognized nearly worldwide. They were the working man's pants. Levi's earliest trademark, burned into a leather patch on every pair, showed two farmers driving workhorses in opposite directions, trying unsuccessfully to tear a pair of Levis apart. Levis were inexpensive, and they wore like iron.

Down through the years updated versions of Levi Jeans have been worn by workers, cowboys, kids, presidents and just about everyone.

At the time of his death, at age 73, lifetime bachelor Levi Strauss left most of his millions to charities.

It wasn't until the middle of the 1950s beginning on college campuses around the country, that blue jeans became a symbol of self-expression – a new found freedom for some, a protest against established society for others. In 1950 they were doing $8 million a year and by 1975 sales for Levi's had topped $1 billion annually. In 1990 they were still selling "like hot-cakes" to the younger generation and were by then commencing to have trouble with counterfeiters.   314

Inventor Goldman: A better mousetrap on wheels.

Super-Mart pioneer store owner, Sidney Goldman, in Oklahoma City in 1936 got the idea of a grocery shopping cart while looking at a folding chair in his office. Shoppers were reluctant to use his twin basket cart until he added a child's seat in 1938.   315

In a Fort Worth, Texas store building, on April 18, 1934, J.F. Cantrell set up four electric washing machines, charging folks by the hour who brought in their dirty clothes for washing. He called the place a "washateria". It worked. Other places opened, but they came to be know as "laundramats".   316

A folding chair sparked his first shopping cart in 1936.

One morning in 1847, fifteen year old Hanson C. Gregory was watching his mother cooking the family's favorite fried cakes in lard, in their Clam Cove, Maine kitchen. As mother Gregory tossed the sizzling cakes on his plate, young Hanson mentioned that the centers had not cooked as well as the outsides. "They never do", his mother told him. The boy took his knife and gouged a hole through the middle of each cake, saying, "then let's do away with the centers", which they did. Thus the doughnut was born in 1847. In 1947 a centennial bronze plaque was placed on the Gregory home where the doughnut was born 100 years previously.   317

Young Gregory thought his mother's fried cakes would cook faster if he gouged a hole in their center.

Chester Greenwood thought folks needed ear mufflers in 1877.

Earmuffs were invented in 1873 by Chester Greenwood of Farmington, Maine, who commenced manufacturing them the following year. He obtained patent number 188,292, March 13, 1877, on his "Ear Mufflers".   318

Mary Jacob preferred to stitch two handkerchiefs together to support her breasts in 1914.

In 1914 Mary Phelps Jacob, a wealthy 19 year old New York debutante, tired of wearing a tightly laced iron staved corset. She stitched two lace handkerchiefs onto a pink silk ribbon that lightly supported her breasts and gently revealed her figure. She was the envy of her friends who wanted her to sew brassieres for them. She applied for a patent on her "brassiere" that she sold to the Warner Brothers Corset Company for $15,000.   319

John B. Stetson made himself a beaver hair hat that would shed rain while panning for gold.

John B. Stetson was a gold miner, who made his first "Stetson", wide-brimmed, high crowned western hat of beaver hair in 1860, to protect him from the sun and rain while panning for gold.   320

Hot Dogs weren't always Hot Dogs.

One day in April 1900 Harry Stevens, who ran the frankfurter stall at the New York Polo Grounds shouted, "They're hot, red hot. Get your dachshund sausages while they're hot." A newspaper cartoonist, Tad Dorgan, hearing Stevens sales pitch, drew a cartoon of two frankfurters barking at each other and titled it "Hot Dogs". They have been hot dogs ever since.   321

"Gayettys Medicated Paper" replaced Sears and Wards catalogs in the "back house".

In 1857 a New York paper salesman, Joseph Gayetty, commenced offering a roll of grey colored manilla hemp paper watermarked with his name "Gayetty's Medicated Paper". He advertised it as "a pure article for the toilet, and a prevention for piles." This was the first toilet paper advertised.   322

CIDER PRESS

Cider could be made more potent by skimming the slush ice off the top.

For reasons unknown, early settlers of North America failed to bring with them from Europe the "whiskey still" as we know it. Their drinks were beer, cider and wine. Beer being made from pumpkins, potatoes, sea plums, Indian corn, carrots and turnips, was sometimes sweetened with honey from wild bee trees and the sap from maple trees. Beer would normally contain from 8% to 12% alcohol. Hard cider was made from crab apples, peaches, plums and pears, with about 5% alcohol. When alcoholic content reaches a maximum of 12% fermentation ceases. Alcoholic content could be increased to 25% by setting the jugs outside in winter and carefully removing the slush ice that would squeeze out of the neck of the frozen jug. Peaches were preferred for this process. Wine was made from wild grapes, elderberries, and currants. It was learned that a cold blanket could be thrown over a boiling kettle of wine and the condensed vapors wrung out into a pail. In this way crude grape, peach and pear brandies were being made by year 1630.

Rum, made from molasses on the sugar plantations of the West Indies, had to be transshipped to the Colonies from England. By 1660 Massachusetts colonies were importing molasses from the West Indies to make their own dark brown, high-proof rum by distillation. As a substitute for rum, New Englanders fermented and distilled honey from native bee trees, called "Old Metheglin," which was dark brown with about 60 percent alcohol, of which Benjamin Franklin supposedly made "delicious" drinks for his lady friends.

Grape, peach and pear brandy could be made by throwing a cold blanket over a boiling kettle of wine and the condensed vapors wrung out into a pail.

It was learned Kentucky mountain lime waters made good whiskey. Who first started making corn liquor in Kentucky in the late 18th century is unknown, but among them were several ministers, such as Rev. Elijah Craig, Baptist minister of Georgetown, Scott County, Kentucky, and his minister brother, Lewis, who supplied liquor to flatboats down the Mississippi River for distribution in New Orleans. There was often discussion as to whether preachers and parishioners should make whiskey. Drunken parishioners at revival meetings, however, were dealt with severely, with possible expulsion from the congregation. A mountain man that made whiskey could use it with which

Paul Revere held the monopoly on making copper whiskey stills until 1802.

In 1858 Virginia election, George Washington won over James Madison by giving voters free liquor and Madison didn't.

In 1794 distillers tarred and feathered collectors of a whiskey tax to pay for the Revolutionary War.

to pay debts and trade for essentials. Silversmith Paul Revere was the only colonial manufacturer of rolled copper for stills and held the monopoly until 1802. For that reason early native stills were fashioned from iron, which made off-color liquor. Proof, or strength, was determined by mixing equal parts of gunpowder and whiskey, then setting it afire. If the preparation flashed up, the whiskey was too strong; if it didn't burn, it was too weak. when it burned evenly the whiskey was considered 100 percent perfect and was called "100 proof." (Since then it has been determined that pure alcohol is 200 proof, as it was learned later that "100 proof" was 50% alcohol.)

In 1758 George Washington learned the value of whiskey in elections, when he won the seat to the Virginia House of Burgesses by giving voters free liquor. James Madison, who ran against Washington, lost presumably because he refused to supply refreshments to voters. In fact, George Washington made peach brandy and rye and corn whiskey on his plantation. His liquors were noted for their good taste. During the Revolutionary War Washington insisted that the army be supplied a liquor ration. when grain was in short supply Washington insisted on rations of peach or apple brandy, or of rum.

In 1791 Alexander Hamilton, then Secretary of Treasury, rammed through Congress an Excise Tax on liquors, "distilled within the United States" to help pay for the Revolutionary War, to which indignation ran high. Many distillers were hailed into court, including the Rev. Elijah Craig, who had a liability of $140 assessed against him. In 1794 distillers and shippers joined forces to oppose the Excise Tax on liquors, which included tarring and feathering liquor tax collectors and shooting up the homes of the excisemen. Hamilton convinced Washington that the whiskey rebels must be crushed and by the fall of 1794 an army of 13,000 troops, armed with artillery, mortars, and whiskey had been mustered and they marched through the Cumberland Gap. Even George Washington appeared on a white horse to show that the government really meant business. The cost was $1.5 million. When Jefferson assumed the presidency in

1801 he repealed the unpopular and often uncollectable whiskey tax and it was not reimposed until during the Civil War. It has never since been removed.

In 1840 E.G. Booz of Philadelphia put the first whiskey in a bottle, shaped like a log cabin. Thus the word "Booz" originated. The Volstead Act (18th Amendment), prohibiting the manufacture or sale of intoxicating liquors in the U.S., was passed October 28, 1919 over President Wilson's veto, after having been ratified by 36 states. On February 20, 1933, after it had been a Roosevelt campaign issue, The Blaine Act to repeal the 18th Amendment was submitted to the states and was adopted in December of that year. This put an end to "blind-pig" saloons, "moonshine", whiskey, 3.2 beer and the gang wars of prohibition days. – Gleaned from "A Nation of Moonshiners" article in Natural History, January 1976.   323

First beer cans in 1935 had bottle caps.

Beer in cans was placed on sale in Richmond, Va., on January 24, 1935.   324

Beer mug lids were originally used to keep flies out of the beer. In most places the flies are gone but lids still close over the tops of ornately decorated mugs (Bierkrugel mit Metall-Deckel).   325

Beer mug lids kept flys out.

The origin of "cocktails" – 1776. During the American Revolution a barmaid garnished Colonial and French officers' drinks on one occasion with the tail feathers of chickens she had stolen from the farm of a neighboring British sympathizer, that she intended to serve the British for dinner. This so delighted one Frenchman at the American table that he cried out, "Vive le coq's tail!" The name stuck and now stands for any drink into which fruit, flavoring, flowers or leaves are mixed – cocktail. Per capita U.S. consumption of liquor declined from approximately three gallons in 1860 to one gallon in 1960.   326

First cocktail was actually a chicken's tail feather.

If you hear someone referring to a "booz" bottle, he's probably talking about the 1860 E.G. Booz cabin bottle that is a collector's item. This bottle and others can be viewed at the Harold Warp Pioneer Village at Minden, Nebraska. 327

HAROLD WARP
PIONEER VILLAGE
Minden, Neb. 68959 FOUNDATION

E.G. Booz really started something when he put whiskey in a bottle.

Fernand Petiot of Canton, Ohio, is the bartender credited with inventing the "Bloody Mary" drink. The year was 1920. The place was Paris and Harry's New York Bar. Bartender Petiot poured a can of tomato juice into an equal portion of vodka – and viola: "We all agreed it was pretty good," recalls Petiot, a bald Frenchman whose accent is now a soothing 3:1 mixture of English and French. "One of the boys suggested we call it Bloody Mary," Petiot explains, "because the drink reminded him of the Bucket of Blood Club in Chicago, and he had a girl named Mary." Petiot brought the drink with him in 1934 when he came to New York to be head bartender at the St. Regis Hotel, a post he held for more than 30 years. There Petiot added seasoning because many New Yorkers considered it too flat. 328

HAROLD WARP
PIONEER VILLAGE
Minden, Neb. 68959 FOUNDATION

The Bucket of Blood Club in Chicago and a girl named Mary sparked "Bloody Mary".

A small Atlanta druggist named John S. Pemberton, looking for a pleasant patent medicine to sell, cooked up a mixture of fruit syrup, extract of Kola nut, plain water, and extract of coca leaf in 1886. He advertised it as a brain and nerve tonic which would cure various stomach disorders and alleviate menstrual distress. In his first year he sold 25 gallons of syrup, grossed $50, and spent $46 for advertising. Shortly before he died in 1888, Pemberton sold Coca-Cola for $1800 to another Atlanta druggist, Asa G. Candler, as well as all rights to the trademarked flowing script. (The script, as well as the name, had been created by Pemberton's bookkeeper, Frank Robinson, who stayed with the company after Candler took over, ultimately becoming treasurer.) In 1891 Candler sold 9,000 gallons of syrup, mostly in the South, after an accidental discovery that the addition of car-

Drink
Coca-Cola
Delicious and Refreshing
5¢
THE COCA-COLA COMPANY, ATLANTA, GA.

Pemberton's Coca-Cola brain and nerve tonic contained cocaine in 1886 when first mixed up in his Atlanta drug store.

Ben Thomas and Joe Whitehead talked Candler into exclusive rights to bottle Coca Cola to sell at ball games in 1899.

Brock Candy Company sued their salesman for "moonlighting" Pepsi-Cola in discarded beer bottles for a nickle.

bonated water at the fountain made Coca-Cola taste better. By 1900 the medicinal properties were replaced with advertising such as a "delicious beverage to be enjoyed," carried on wall clocks, calendars, fans, bookmarks, blotters, and metal trays featuring pretty girls in their teens drinking "Coke". Coca-Cola, in the early 1900s, had to overcome claims that it was a "dope" because it did carry small traces of cocaine and some caffeine in the extracts from the coca leaf and kola nut.

Two men, Ben Thomas and Joe Whitehead, saw the possibility of selling coca-cola in bottles at ball games, so in 1899 they obtained exclusive rights from Candler to sell Coca-cola in bottles. The hobble-skirt bottle was designed in 1913 by a glassblower named Samuelson who worked for an Indiana glass company, patented in November 1915, and adopted by Coca-Cola in 1916.

As years went by Asa Candler gave stock to his family and in 1919 the family sold Coca-Cola to a group headed by Ernest Woodruff of Atlanta for $25 million. Asa Candler did not want to sell but his family overruled him.

During the 1920s a struggling competitor "Pepsi-Cola" could have been purchased by Coca-Cola for very little. In the early 1930s Pepsi-Cola reorganized for the third time. When Prohibition ended in 1933, a Brock Candy salesman in Chicago began filling discarded beer bottles, advertising by radio "Pepsi-Cola hits the spot, 12 full ounces, that's a lot, for a nickel-nickel-nickel," wherever they could get distribution. Brock sued him claiming he worked for Brock but they lost. Pepsi-Cola began to sell and Coca-Cola sued for trademark infringement. Coca-Cola lost because they placed their trademark wrongfully in the tail of the C in "Coca." The court ruled this protected "Coca" but not "Cola," giving Pepsi free use of "Cola". In 1975 both companies had dropped the "Cola" portion of their names and that year sales of "Coke" were over $2½ billion and "Pepsi" sales were over $2 billion. Which just goes to show how John Pemberton's Coca-Cola brain tonic became a big business in beverages between 1886 and 1975. – Portions gleaned from Tropic, Article by Lawrence Dietz 4-20-69. 329

In 1809 Nicholas Appert, a Frenchman, discovered that foods could be preserved by boiling them in glass containers and sealing them tight with a waxed cork before cooling. The French Government paid him 12,000 francs (about $4,000) for his discovery and he patented it. In 1823 Thomas Kersett patented the first tin can method of preserving foods. The first items preserved in tin cans were lobsters and salmon, followed by fruits and Pennsylvania.

Early Fruit Jars

Nick Appert discovered foods could be preserved in glass jars.

In 1855 Robert Arthur invented a saucer-shaped tin lid that fit into a groove in the mouth of the jar. This was covered with melted wax to seal in the contents. On November 23, 1858, Patent #22,129 and on November 30, 1858, Mr. Mason patented and introduced the zinc screw cap, #22,186, but it was Lewis R. Boyd who thought of putting a glass liner in Mason's zinc cap in 1869 to prevent the food from having a "tinny" taste. Boyd probably got the idea of the glass liner after Salmon B. Rowley, in 1868, invented a glass lid that was partially covered with a metal screw band, similar to jar lids of a hundred years later. Mason's name continued to be used on fruit jars, although he seemed uninterested in overcoming the metallic taste of his zinc lids. His Mason Manufacturing Company was taken over by Consolidated Fruit Jar Company in 1870 and they retained the "Mason" trademark. Other jars came on the market, such as "Air Tight," "All-Right," and "Darling" but the "Mason" continued to be the most popular.

Mason's Zinc Lid

Melted wax sealed the jars until Mr. Mason made a zinc screw lid in 1858 and Mr. Boyd put a glass liner in Mason's lid in 1869.

In 1886 the five Ball brothers, William, Frank, Lucius, Edmond and George, built the Ball Brothers Glass Works in Buffalo, N.Y., to make jars with both Mason's and Rowley's glass topped lids. Their factory burned in 1887 and the following year they opened their factory in Muncie, Indiana where they have continued to make "Ball Brothers" and "Mason" canning jars down through the years. Mason's patent number continued to appear on fruit jars long after his patent ran out and even after his death in 1902, as a charity case in New York City. 330

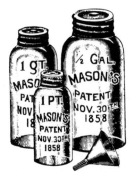

In 1886 the five Ball brothers took over Mason jars, but continued to sell both "Mason" and "Ball Bros." fruit jars.

HAROLD WARP PIONEER VILLAGE FOUNDATION
Minden, Neb. 68959

Seeing a little Mexican girl chewing paraffin prompted Thomas Adams to quit trying to make rubber from the sap of the Sapodilla tree (Mexicans called it Chicle) so he kneaded it into little balls, that he gave his druggist to try to sell at a penny a piece. Adams never tried to make rubber again.

When the milklike latex of the rubber tree was selling for $1 a pound shortly after the Civil War, Thomas Adams, Civil War photographer, glass merchant and self-confessed inventor was trying to make rubber from the Mexican sapodilla sap instead, that cost only five cents a pound. He finally gave up and contemplated dumping the "chicle", as the Mexicans called it, into the ocean. However, one afternoon in a Hoboken drugstore he saw a little girl chewing paraffin and recalled seeing a Mexican chomping a pinch of chicle. Adams asked the druggist if he'd like to sell a better gum. "Sure, if you've got any," said the druggist. "Paraffin isn't a very good chew." Horatio Adams, his son who died in 1956 at the age of 102, reported, "That evening my father and I took some of the chicle and put it into hot water. We left it there until it was about the consistency of putty. Then we wet our hands, rubbed and kneaded it and finally rolled it into little balls – two hundred of them. It was no longer brownish black, but a kind of grayish white. We sent the balls to the druggist. A few days later he told us they were selling well at a penny apiece." Encouraged, Adams rented a Jersey City factory loft. Kneaded and rolled by hand – and quite tasteless – the gum was put up in boxes labeled: Adams' New York Gum – Snapping and Stretching. An inveterate tinkerer, Adams built a machine to knead his gum, then settled down to find a way to flavor it. He tried sassafras, then licorice, which he shredded into the chickle. By 1870 "Yucatan", "Kiss-Me" and "Tucee-Kiss" were on sale, along with his "Adams' Black Jack," which is the oldest flavored gum still on the market.

A Cleveland, Ohio druggist, Dr. Edward E. Beeman, manufactured a pepsin compound, and one day his bookkeeper Nellie Horton, urged him to put it into gum "since so many people buy pepsin for digestion and gum for no reason at all." Beeman succeeded in blending chicle with pepsin. His pepsin compound wrapper featured a pig's picture – the idea being that if you took his pepsin, you could eat like a pig! He put the same pig's picture on his gum wrapper! Nevertheless, the gum sold. One day Beeman showed his books to George Worthington, who offered to refinance and reorganize the company. Beeman accepted. Worthington put Beeman's bearded face on the wrapper in place of the pig. Beeman became an overnight celebrity. Although Beeman died in 1906, his picture was not removed from the package until a few years ago by American Chicle, its present owners.

A Cleveland popcorn salesman, William J. White, revolutionized gum making. White made the discovery that solved the flavor problem forever, and made him a millionaire. Since chicle itself would not absorb flavors, he found that by combining flavors with corn syrup, any flavor could be obtained, and the syrup then blended instantly with chicle. White decided on peppermint flavor for his "Yellow Band Gum", later called "Yucatan", which was an instantaneous success. Those who survived, including Adams, had to adopt White's flavoring technique. Even today more than fifty percent of all gum sold is peppermint. White organized the American Chicle Company and drew into his combine all the leading companies – his own, Adams', Beeman's, and Chiclets, the candy-coated gum tablet first introduced in 1890. The tycoons of the gum trust relaxed – not knowing they were about to be hit by a bombshell in the form of a soap salesman.

The soap salesman was twenty-nine year old William Wrigley, Jr. Knowing people dreamed of getting something for nothing, he offered a free can of baking powder with his soap. When he saw people wanted the baking powder more than the soap, he shifted – sold baking powder and gave away two packets of chewing gum. When he saw his customers were more interested in gum than in baking powder, he shifted again, into the gum business. He had the Zeno Gum Company manufacture two brand names for him: "Vassar" for the "classy" trade, and "Lotta" for those who wanted a lot. As his sales grew he took over the Zeno plant. Nice people rejected gum as "unsightly". Tobacco chewers called it "sissy". For years the gum-chewing doll on stage symbolized a lady of loose morals. Tales circulated that gum was really composed of horses' hooves and glue, and that if accidentally swallowed would cause indigestion, appendicitis, or the intestines to "stick together",

Twenty-nine year old soap salesman Wm. Wrigley Jr. offered a free can of baking powder with his soap. Folks preferred his "baking powder", so he started selling baking powder and gave two packets of chewing gum with it. When he saw people preferred his gum, he had the Zeno Gum Company make "Vassa" for the classy and "Lotta" for bargain hunters. He wound up buying the Zeno factory and dropped baking powder.

resulting in death. Many a youngster, having accidentially swallowed his gum, sat down somberly to await The End!

After nine lean years, Wrigley made two momentous decisions in 1907. One was to stop chasing flavors and concentrate on selling of spearmint-flavored gum which he had introduced. His second decision defied business-like reasoning. As the depression of 1907 developed, he decided to embark on a gigantic advertising campaign since reduction of the trust's advertising would make his at least twice as noticeable. He borrowed and mortgaged everything he owned. He unleashed the first spectacular national advertising campaign this country had ever seen, featuring a spear-like, grinning gnome which he designed himself. If dealers properly displayed his gum, the battle was won. Therefore, with every bulk purchase of his gum, he offered a dazzling selection of premiums. He also sent two sticks of his gum to every name in the nation's phone books. When Wrigley's initial spectacular campaign broke, the gum tycoons went right on crimping their advertising budgets, thereby making one of the biggest blunders in the history of American business. Even when it was apparent that they were being threatened with collapse, they went right on taking twenty percent of the gross for their profits instead of putting it into sales campaigns. Meanwhile Wrigley's sales jumped from $170,000 to $1,345,000 in his first year and he was on his way to leadership in the chewing gum industry.

Wrigley found that spearmint flavor lasted longest, so during the 1907 money panic he sent two sticks of gum to every name in the nation's phone books. He also doubled his advertising to become leader in the gum industry.

The eighty-foot sapodilla tree must reach the age of seventy years before it can be tapped, thrives only in the jungle, and can be tapped only every five years. Incidentally, the chewiness of gums varies greatly. "Black Jack", for instance, is "slippery" while "Dentyne" is "stiff." The first bubble gum appeared in 1906 named "Blibber-blubber!" However, its "wet" bubble stuck so tenaciously to faces and lips when it burst that only hard scrubbing could remove it. Hence, it lacked return sales. In 1928, the F.H. Fleer Company perfected a "dry" bubble gum. Gaining elasticity through use of a harmless synthetic rubber, similar to that in tires, it made perfect bubbles! Called "Double-Bubble", it was a sensational success and still dominates children's gum buying. The chicle shortage created by World War II caused gum companies to embark on heavy scientific programs to perfect plastic resins, similar to tree saps. After the war few went back to chicle. Thus, what we are chewing today is largely synthetic plastic, chiefly polyvinyl acetate.

331

William Procter came from England and James Gamble from Ireland, as immigrants in the early 19th century. They settled in Cincinnati, then referred to as "Porkopolis", as it was a major hog butchering center. Procter worked as a soap-maker's apprentice, and Gamble as a candle-maker's helper. In 1883 they married sisters of a local chandler, Alexander Norris. Four years later, in 1837, when Procter was 35 and Gamble 34, they each put up $3600 to enter a partnership to make soap and candles. Procter ran the office, Gamble managed the manufacturing, and by 1848 their earnings were $27,000 that year. By 1859, with salesmen criss-crossing the country, they were the largest business in Cincinnati, with annual sales over $1 million. They lived into their eighties. Procter's sons and grandsons ran P&G until 1930, when Richard Deupree became the first non-family executive.

332

Mr. Procter

Mr. Gamble

Two immigrants, Procter from England and Gamble from Ireland, married sisters of a soap and candle maker, in 1883. Four years later they opened their own store, with $3600 each. Procter, 35, ran the office and Gamble, 34, made the soap and candles. But not for long. By 1848 their earning reached $27,000.

Roman men removed dirt from their skin with a scraper and Roman ladies bathed in strawberry juice. "Sapo" (soap) is credited to an Arabian, Iban Dschanbir, in the ninth century.

Soap, as we know it, was not used until the ninth century. Mention of soap or "sapo" is credited to an Arabian alchemist, Ibn Hajan Dschanbir, during that century. Under Charles the Great soap craftsmen in Marseilles supplied their products to the royal estates. During the fourteenth century Venice captured the soap making crown. Vegetable and animal oils were used. Eventually perfumes were added in an attempt to improve the odor and symbols (trade marks) were carved on the surface, such as spheres, sun, half moon, and even lilies to symbolize a lush perfumed soap. Romans removed the dirt from the skin with a scraper. Roman ladies were known to bathe in a concoction of twenty pounds of crushed strawberries and two pounds of crushed raspberries – but no soap.

333

The Sorghum Mill
Refined cane sugar came during the Civil War and beet sugar was first refined in 1890s.

He discovered Saccharine in his mustache.

Chemist Schlatter discovered Aspartame when he licked his finger to pick up a piece of paper in 1965.

"Microwave" was discovered when a steel worker's candy bar melted when he laid it near his welder.

Clarence Birdseye, while in the Arctic in 1925 found the meat of a caribou that had been frozen for months still tasted tender and fresh.

There was no such thing as refined white sugar prior to the Civil War. Refined cane sugar was first made in 1857 for Civil War soldiers and beet sugar was first refined in the 1890s. You can see how bees make honey and how sorghum molasses was made, before sugar was refined, at the Harold Warp Pioneer Village at Minden in south central Nebraska. 334

A Mallinckrodt chemist's mustache accidentally blew in his mouth while crossing a bridge in St. Louis on his way home from work one night in the 1920s. It tasted sweet, thus saccharine was discovered. 335

In December 1965, chemist James M. Schlatter was working on a project to develop a new anti-ulcer drug at the laboratories of G.D. Searle. "I licked my finger to pick up a piece of paper and my finger tasted good," he recalls. That's how he discovered the low-calorie sweetener. "Aspartame." 336

During World War II a steel worker, who was eating a candy bar, found that it melted when he laid it on a steel beam while he was welding it. The microwaves from the electric generator had melted his candy bar. Thus the microwave oven was discovered. 337

In 1925 Clarence Birdseye noticed a piece of caribou meat that had been frozen in the Arctic for several months, was still tender and fresh flavored. Being a chemist, he figured it had been rapidly frozen at a low temperature. He was right, and he sold his "Birdseye" quick freeze process to General Foods in 1930. The first home freezer was the "Deep-Freeze" made in Waukegan, Illinois, introduced in 1942. 338

Lye Maker

For centuries, lye was made by dumping fireplace wood ashes into a wooden structure with a cone shaped opening at the bottom. Lye would ooze out of the bottom of the cone into a hollowed out log, as rain water saturated the ashes. 339

HAROLD WARP
PIONEER VILLAGE
Minden, Neb. 68959 FOUNDATION

Grated starch settled to the bottom of the tub.

Starch was made by early settlers with a potato grater using well washed potatoes. The potatoes would be grated into a tub of water. The starch would settle to the bottom, leaving the floating pulp to be skimmed off. The pure white starch would then be removed from the bottom of the tub and dried. 340

HAROLD WARP
PIONEER VILLAGE
Minden, Neb. 68959 FOUNDATION

Europeans thought tobacco had medicinal value.

Tobacco development and decline – Used by Indians since remote times, tobacco was first brought to Spain and France in 1559 by Nicot, and to England in 1585 by Drake. It was first thought to have medicinal value, but soon became a luxury. It became a major export crop for early colonial settlers and was actually used as currency in Jamestown, Virginia in the 1600s. In the West Indies, Cubans were rolling "cigars" when white men arrived. They were irregularly shaped in various sizes that eventually found their way to Europe, packed in barrels and sold for one cent to two cents each. They resembled pieces of pitch blackened rope and are still sold in remote areas.

"Snuff" became popular in Europe. Even royalty indulged in a "sniff of snuff", that would be placed on the back of the hand and quickly drawn into one nostril as the back of the hand held the other nostril closed. Fancy snuff boxes were the vogue of the eighteenth century. Most Americans preferred to dab a cherry stick in the snuff box, and place it inside the cheek with a portion protruding. The fibers of the cherry twig remaining in the mouth would separate similarly to the hairs of a brush, which would hold the snuff in a ball. As late as the 1920s it was not uncommon to see an elderly "plantation" lady with a respectable air about her, having a "cherry stick" protruding from the corner of her snuff darkened lips. Rugged outdoor men

A man who rolled Bull Durham cigarettes was either a "dandy" or a "thug".

Machine made Cincos sold for 5¢.

"Tailor made cigarettes" wound up in stores everywhere after World War I, when the boys in service got them free.

Prince Albert and Velvet were preferred by pipe smokers.

Conestoga wagon drivers made their own stogies.

chewed "Horse-Shoe", "Piperheidsie" and "Star" plug tobacco, while financial tycoons smoked "Stogies" and the more expensive hand rolled "Havanas." Cigars were first made by machine in 1916, "Cinco" being a leading brand made by machine, selling for five cents each. Cigar sales reached their peak in the United States in 1920. Then cigarette smoking gained in popularity and cigar smoking declined.

At the turn of the twentieth century a young man who smoked cigarettes was either considered a "dandy" or a "thug". He wasn't just an ordinary person. Bull Durham attached a package of cigarette papers to the side of their cloth bag that contained dry cut tobacco. Dukes Mixture followed suit. In time Prince Albert and Valvet, that both came in cans to fit the pocket, commenced giving away a package of cigarette papers with each can of tobacco. "Camels" were trying to get public acceptance, but "roll your owns" predominated in most areas until after World War I. During the war soldiers everywhere were suddenly smoking "tailor-made cigarettes." When they returned home tailor-made cigarettes followed the boys into restaurant counters and drugstores. The leaders were Camels, Chesterfield, Lucky Strike and Spurs. Cigarettes were also donated to soldiers in World War II. Women were educated through advertising, to smoke cigarettes during the 1930s. Probably what made smoking popular and fashionable among ladies, more than any other thing, was a simple eight word advertisement designed by George Washington Hill, President of American Tobacco Company: "Reach for a Lucky instead of a sweet." By the 1970s a leading cause of death was throat and lung cancer, caused by smoking cigarettes. By 1990 cigarette smoking was banned in most offices and public places. 341

HAROLD WARP
PIONEER VILLAGE
Minden, Neb. 68959 FOUNDATION

Cigars got their "stogie" nickname from the Conestoga wagons used to haul freight in the last century. The wagoneers bought tobacco during their trips and fashioned the long, dark cigars that bear the nickname. 342

When Cornelius Vanderbilt, in 1853, wanted his fried potatoes sliced thinner, the chef really fried them paper thin. But it was Bill Tappenden that first put them in a paper bag in 1895.

Cacao beans in the pod.

Chocolate was first made in Holland in 1828, although Cocoa was brought to Europe from the South American Cacao tree in the 16th century.

While a French waitress, Miss Suzette was serving an order of pancakes, soaked in brandy, the restaurant owner decided to ignite the brandy to show it was for real.

First Sundae 1885.

One evening in 1853 Cornelius Vanderbilt, while eating in a Saratoga Springs, New Jersey restaurant, told the chef his fried potatoes were cut too thick. The irate chef then served Vanderbilt his potatoes cut paper thin, fried to a crisp and heavily salted. Vanderbilt liked them and they became a staple restaurant item for the next 40 years. Then in 1895 William Tappenden started cooking potato chips in his kitchen and delivering them in paper bags to local grocery stores. Soon his kitchen was too small, so he converted his barn to the first potato chip factory. When the Japanese invaded Pearl Harbor, one of the leading potato chip makers at that time changed the name from "Jap's Potato Chips" to "Jays".   343

Cocoa has always been a commodity tinged with romance. Originating in Central America, cocoa comes from the cacao tree. It was brought to Spain by the conquistadors in the 16th century. Its popularity boomed with the Dutch invention of chocolate candy in 1828. Today most of the world's cocoa supply comes from West Africa, where the Ivory Coast ranks as the leading exporter; other African producers include Ghana and Cameroon. Brazil and Malaysia are also major suppliers.   344

Crepes Suzette – A French actress, Mademoiselle Suzette, is honored by this dish. While playing the part of a servant at the Comedie Francaise in the 1890s, she served pancakes (crepes) in one scene. The restaurant proprietor who supplied them had the idea of igniting them with brandy to show that the pancakes were real, thus Suzette won immortality.   345

Ice cream sundaes were invented in 1885 in Evanston, Ill., when selling soda was banned on Sundays.   346

First malted milk 1883.

First toothpaste tube 1892.

On September 26, 1820 Col. Johnson ate a tomato to prove it wasn't poisonous.

Chicken à la King

The nation's first malted milk is claimed to have been made by William Horlick in Racine, Wisconsin in 1883. 347

Screw cap bottle with a pourlip was patented by E.A. Ravenscroft on May 5, 1936. 348

Dr. Washington Wentworth Sheffield, a dentist in New London, Conn., is credited with inventing the collapsible metal toothpaste tube in 1892. 349

"Tootsie" was the Viennese sweetheart of an Austrian candy maker named Leo Hirshfield. He left her to seek his fortune in New York City in 1896, and when his candy roll caught on, he named it "Tootsie Roll" for his girlfriend. 350

Originally, tomatoes came from tropical South America, primarily from Peru. In Europe, they were first called molas peruvianna and pomi del peru. The name tomato comes from the Aztec word tomatl. Although a staple of Italy since the 1500s, tomatoes were considered highly poisonous in this country and were grown for ornamental purposes until September 26, 1820, when, according to record, Colonel Robert Gibbon Johnson became the first American to eat a tomato in public. He did so standing on the courthouse steps in Salem, New Jersey, before the eyes of a gaping crowd. The tomato was also known as pomme d'amour, the love apple. 351

Chicken a la King – The word king was originally Keane. Some decades ago, the polo player Foxhall Keane suggested this way of serving chicken to the chef of Delmonico's restaurant in New York City. The dish was named chicken a la Keane, but through the years Keane has become king. 352

Bloomington Land Office.

In 1876 John N. Warp would get his 80 acre "Timber-Claim" free if he kept 20 acres of Ash trees alive for 8 years.

Bloomington Land Office – Where Homesteaders Filed. During the 1870s and 1880s homesteaders came to the prairie states by the thousands, Harold Warp's father among them. He filed for an 80 acre "Timber Claim" in 1876 in Kearney County, Nebraska. In order to get the 80 acres free of charge he had to keep 20 acres of ash trees alive on these treeless plains for eight years before title to the land was given to him in 1885. John N. Warp filed for his homestead in the sandstone government building that stood at Bloomington, Nebraska, just as hundreds of homesteaders did. This sandstone building was moved to the Harold Warp Pioneer Village Foundation at Minden, Nebraska in 1950. Since then millions of fascinated visitors have gone through it. (John N. Warp lived in a "dugout" on a hillside of his 80 acres while proving up on it, just as many of the early settlers did.) 353

Sod houses once dotted the plains states where wood was scarce. They are now almost all gone, but one has been reconstructed with its interior appropriately furnished, at the Harold Warp Pioneer Village at Minden, in south central Nebraska, where millions of people have marveled at the ingenuity of our pioneer forebears who built this great country of ours. It took nine acres of sod to build this sodhouse at the Harold Warp Pioneer Village, located 12 miles south of I-80 at the Minden, Nebraska exit in south central Nebraska. 354

The Sod House

It took 3 men 3 weeks in 1955 and 9 acres of sod to duplicate a sod house built for $39 in 1880.

Immigrants who arrived from the East at the historic Lowell Depot to homestead Nebraska prairies rode in the same cars in which the buffalo hides and the range cattle were shipped out to the East. The Lowell Depot that has seven worn out floors, one on top of the other, has been saved for posterity by one individual, Harold Warp, who moved it to his Pioneer Village at Minden, in south central Nebraska in 1950, which was converted to a non-profit, historic foundation in 1983. 355

Lowell Depot

Homesteaders arrived at this depot in the 1870s and 1880s in the same railroad cars in which range cattle and buffalo hides were shipped east.

Huge windmills furnished water for locomotives.

Huge windmills stood beside depots across the country during the days of steam locomotives, to furnish water to make steam to pull them with. The very last of these Union Pacific windmills was saved from destruction by Harold Warp and moved 351 miles from Agate, Colo., to his Pioneer Village at Minden, in south central Nebraska in 1953, where it can pump water for the Village Green. 356

Pumpkin Creek relay station now at Warp's Pioneer Village.

Millions of visitors have passed through the old Pony Express Station at the Harold Warp Pioneer Village, Nebraska's #1 tourist attraction located at Minden, in south central Nebraska. This station was the Pumpkin Creek Relay Station to the Black Hills. It houses a "mochilla" used by Pony Express riders as well as Buffalo Bill's saddle and a steel money box that was built into Wells Fargo stages.

Early day druggists grew herbs in back yard and made paint in the basement.

Today very few drugstores can be found that do not have cosmetics, cameras as well as a myriad of notions. Prior to 1900, Apothecary shops were likely to have herbs growing in the back yard, shelves full of patent medicines and drawers full of sassafras, cinnamon sticks and rock candy from which the proprietor concocted medicines and made pills. In their basement many druggists ground and mixed house paints. An 1850 Apothecary shop can be visited at the historical Harold Warp Pioneer Village non-profit Foundation in south central Nebraska. 358

1910 Kitchen
Every daughter wants a more modern kitchen than her mother.

The domestic daughter's desire to do better than mom is portrayed in the kitchen. As evidence, kitchens as well as living rooms and bedrooms of each generation (20 rooms in all) are a part of the Harold Warp Pioneer Village; a huge display of authentic Americana in south central Nebraska. These twenty Pioneer Village period rooms, from 1830 to 1980, trace America's cultural and mechanical development. 359

Here you can actually "walk down through history" and see how America grew.

The #1 tourist attraction in Nebraska is Pioneer Village, on U.S. 6 at Minden, which consists of 26 buildings on 20 acres with more than 50,000 historic items, all of which can be seen by walking less than a mile. Many visitors recommend Warp's Pioneer Village over Ford's museum or Smithsonian Institute. It was converted to a non-profit Historic Foundation by Mr. Warp in 1983 and is located 12 miles south of I-80 at the Pioneer Village exit, in south central Nebraska. 360

Barbed wire kept homesteader's livestock in and range cattle out.

Most notable reasons for the settlement of the Great American Desert (land west of the Mississippi and east of the Rockies) can be attributed to the windmill and barbed wire. The windmill provided water, while barbed wire kept homesteaders' livestock in and range cattle out. A complete collection of all different kinds of barbed wire and representative windmills, including the revolutionary aermotor type, can be viewed at the Harold Warp Pioneer Village non-profit Foundation at Minden in south central Nebraska. 361

From 50 million buffalo, Buffalo Bill kept the railroad builders supplied with meats, but by 1905 Teddy Roosevelt had 15 buffalo shipped west from the New York City Zoo to restock a herd.

When white men first arrived on the plains there were approximately 50,000,000 buffalo in Nebraska and Kansas. By 1900 there were less than 1,000 buffalo left in the entire United States. The massive herds that had stopped railroad trains on the plains were wantonly slaughtered to almost complete extinction between 1860 and 1880. Young William F. Cody was hired by the builders of the railroad to slaughter them. Thus he got his nickname "Buffalo Bill". Millions were killed for the tongue only. Over 20,000,000 buffalo hides were shipped to market in the ten years between 1860 and 1870 at less than $1.00 each. When President Theodore Roosevelt asked that the bison be saved from extinction, "Seed Stock" – fifteen animals – in 1905 had to be shipped to Kansas from New York City's Bronx Zoo, of all places, to establish the Wichita Refuge. 362

500 Fascinating Facts

Buffalo bones were shipped east by the trainload.

Between 1870 and 1875, the bones of 21,000,000 buffalo were shipped east from Kansas and Nebraska at an average price of $100.00 per rail car load, to be used for chicken feed (lime) and lampblack.   363

The first church in Minden, Nebraska, in 1884, was originally called "German Lutheran Church". During World War I the name was changed to "St. Paul Lutheran Church". It is now the Pioneer Village Church, moved there in 1950. Non-denominational services have been held in it every summer Sunday since 1970.   364

Churches had platforms out front for folks to dismount onto.

Early settlers' churches had a wooden platform with steps for women to dismount from conestogas, lumber wagons and horseback.   365

80 pupils were registered in 1890, taught by one $20 per month teacher, in the Grom School.

Almost gone from the American scene is the little Prairie schoolhouse, which was also a meeting place and community center, and imparted the "3 R's" to early settlers' offspring. Typical was the Grom School, moved to the Harold Warp Pioneer Village, Minden, Nebraska, where, with its vintage lunch buckets, antique desks and kerosene lamps, it led to 25 other buildings and more than 50,000 historical items that show "How America Grew."   366

When rain water froze in the holes drilled by homesteaders, the limestone would break apart into fence posts.

Limestone fence posts were common in Kansas in homesteading days to keep livestock in and range cattle out. To make the posts, outcropping limestone would be drilled with holes by hand, about a foot apart, longitudinally. In cold weather these holes would fill with water. When the water froze the ice would expand to break the limestone into slabs that could be used for fence posts.   367

Kids would not ride on lions and tigers; they preferred ponies.

Steam-operated American Carrousel—1880

FIRST STEAM MERRY-GO-ROUND

Early Merry-Go-Rounds had lions and tigers and all kinds of carved animals, but it was discovered that kids preferred ponies to ride on. The oldest steam operated Merry-Go-Round in existence still gives kids of all ages a ride for only a nickel at the Harold Warp Pioneer Village in Minden, Nebraska. 368

The first Pony Express, left on April 3, 1860, St. Joseph for San Francisco, between which places the schedule allowed eight days. Stations averaging at first twenty-five miles apart were established, and each rider was expected to cover seventy-five miles a day. Eventually there were 190 stations, 200 station keepers, 200 assistant station keepers, 80 riders (who were paid from $100 to $125 per month), and between 400 and 500 horses. The quickest trip was that made for the delivery of President Lincoln's Inaugural Address, the distance between St. Joseph, Missouri and Sacramento, California, about 1,400 miles, being covered in seven days and seventeen hours. At first the company charged $5 for each half ounce, but later the charge was reduced to $2.50. The regular Pony Express service was discontinued on the completion of the line of the Pacific Telegraph Company, in October, 1861. The service was often interrupted by Indian hostilities and was extremely hazardous for riders and for station keepers alike. Many were killed. The freighting firm of Russell, Majors and Waddell lost $200,000 on the Pony Express, which was one of their ventures. Buffalo Bill was one of the riders. He once rode 322 miles in twenty-two hours. He changed horses twenty-one times. 369

From St. Joe to Frisco took 8 days and letters cost $5 per half ounce. That's why Pony Express letters were so thin with no envelopes.

Each leather Mochilla contained 4 padlocked mail pouches, that was thrown from one saddle to the other, when riders changed horses.

A rope-tied bed that utilized a corn husk or straw packed mattress is a far cry from our innerspring, cushioned mattress of today. 370

We had straw mattresses in summer and cornhusk mattresses in winter.

First washing machine was an upside down funnel on a stick, patented in 1877.

In 1899 an ad in a Syracuse, N.Y., newspaper stated, "Ten minutes of Easy effort washes a tub of clothes." Thus "Easy" became the name of a washing machine. Twenty-two years previously, Cyrus Dodge, who perfected the "Easy" washer had obtained a patent (in 1877) on a stick in the small end of an ordinary household funnel for washing clothes by suction. 371

HAROLD WARP
PIONEER VILLAGE
Minden, Neb. 68959 FOUNDATION

There was no right or left shoe before the Civil War.

Right or left shoe! It made no difference prior to the Civil War what shoe you picked to put on your foot. Each shoe was made from the same last. The early Cobbler's Shop featured at the Harold Warp Pioneer Village in south central Nebraska features cobblers machines, tools and lasts of the 1840 era. 372

HAROLD WARP
PIONEER VILLAGE
Minden, Neb. 68959 FOUNDATION

A state border dispute is responsible for the "Teddy Bear".

In 1902 Clifford Berryman, cartoonist for the Washington Star, drew a cartoon showing President Theodore Roosevelt refusing to shoot a bear cub, while out bear hunting in Mississippi. He had gone there to settle a border dispute between Louisiana and Mississippi. Morris Michtom, proprietor of a small store in Brooklyn, saw the cartoon. He and his wife forthwith made a bear of honey-colored plush, stuffed with excelsior. He put it in his window alongside a copy of the cartoon. Next the enterprising Michtom wrote to Roosevelt and asked permission to call his animal Teddy Bear. President Roosevelt wrote back and said, "I doubt if my name will mean much in the stuffed bear business, but you may use it if you wish." (A copy of this letter was still in Ideal's files 12-17-61.) Ideal Toy Corporation grew from Michtom's small Brooklyn store. 373

He started Time, Life and Fortune magazines.

HAROLD WARP
PIONEER VILLAGE
Minden, Neb. 68959 FOUNDATION

Time magazine was started by Henry R. Luce in 1923, with the help of a friend. He also started "Life" and "Fortune" in 1936 and Sports Illustrated in 1954. 374

Proof that people resent change.

To prove that people resent change, the first Omnibus (depot hack) made in 1829, resembled a stage coach, as did the first buggies and also railroad passenger cars. The early horseless carriages (autos) not only resembled carriages, but even had dash boards and a whip socket. Some early farm tractors could be driven with leather lines, just as horses had been driven. Examples are on display at the Harold Warp Pioneer Village in Minden, Nebraska. 375

Chicago's first drinking water system was placed in operation in 1842 at a cost of $24,000. It consisted of an intake pipe, 150 feet out in the lake from Lake Street, which supplied water to an elevated wooden tank, from which it flowed by gravity through wooden pipes to paying customers. Only a small portion of the city near the Chicago river was served. A section of Chicago's first water pipe was uncovered in 1959, while removing dirt for a new Loop skyscraper. The wood was in perfect condition and the bark was all intact on this log when it was dug up 117 years after being laid under Chicago's main street in 1842. That log is now on display at the non-profit Harold Warp Pioneer Village Historical Foundation at Minden, Nebraska. 376

Chicago's wooden water pipes good as new after being buried 117 years.

Bill Griebenow was a Chicago fireman for 40 years when fire engines were pulled by three horses. When a fire alarm came in and the alarm was sounded at the firehouse, it would also spring open the horse-stall gates. Each of the three horses would take its respective place to pull the fire engine and the harness that hung overhead would be dropped over the horses and snapped on by the firemen who had slid down the pipe from upstairs. When the chain across the firehouse door would be dropped, the three steeds would dive forward in unison with the firemen hanging on to the clanging fire wagon. Bill said a new horse would learn to do this in just a few days. They didn't have to be taught. Goose

The steam fire engine, 1880.

The three firehouse steeds rarin' to take their places to pull the fire engine when the whistle blew.

grease and sulphur was carried aboard to sooth burns on the horses' backs, caused by sparks and burning embers. Chicago's horse drawn fire engine #17 and the overhead harness that went to many Chicago fires is now at Nebraska's #1 attraction, the Harold Warp Pioneer Village at Minden in south central Nebraska. 377

Harold Warp's father built a cattle and horse barn in 1888, nine miles southeast of Minden, Nebraska. His neighbor, Mike Olson, helped build it. When they started laying the haymow floor, one of Harold's older brothers remarked, "Dad, can we have a barn dance when the barn is finished?" As the Warp children's parents and their neighbors were good Christians, they considered barn dancing and card playing sinful. Therefore, when a barn dance was suggested John Warp and Mike Olson decided right then and there that they would prevent any barn dancing on that haymow floor, so they laid the boards in the haymow floor upside down, with the rough side up. Harold's job as a child was to push back the hay in the mow, and he never realized until after his parents passed away and their home was broken up when he was eleven, that other haymows were much smoother. 378

Dad turned the hayloft floor boards upside down so we kids couldn't have barn dances.

At 14, Kemmons Wilson lost his father, quit school and went to work. His first venture was a popcorn machine, purchased for $50, to be paid for at $1 per week. As years went by he branched out into pinball machines and several theaters. After a stint as World War II pilot, he borrowed $350,000 to build the first Holiday Inn on Summer Street in Memphis in 1952. It really cost only $250,000 to build and within 12 months he had built three more. His goal was 400 Holiday Inns across the country. By 1964 there were 500 and by 1975 there were 1700 Holiday Inns world-wide. The original one by then had been torn down. His motto "You don't learn to sail on a smooth sea." 379

Kemmons Wilson quit school when 14 and sold popcorn before he built 1700 Holiday Inn motels. During a 1951 family vacation he told his wife "I'm going to build motels for travelers and allow kids free."

James Macie Smithson, Smithsonian founder, never set foot in America.

James Macie Smithson, British mineralogist who never set foot in America, willed when he died in 1829 that an estate of $515,169 be used for the "increase and diffusion of knowledge among men" in the U.S.A. Seventeen years later, in 1846, by an act of Congress, the "Smithsonian Institution" was established to use Smithson's gift to the United States. He was born in France, an illegitimate son of Elizabeth Keate Macie and the Duke of Northumberland. Smithson's bequest to America remains a mystery. Joseph Henry, a noted scientist was Smithsonian's first director. 380

Horatio Alger, Jr., 1832-1899.

Horatio Alger Jr. inspired boys by the millions to make something of themselves, including this writer.

Horatio Alger, Jr. (1832-1899) inspired boys everywhere with 123 novels he wrote between 1868 and 1896. His heroes were about 15 years old, orphaned, a country boy or from a destitute family. His heroes usually outsmarted snobs and bullies with honesty, hard work and initiative to go from rags to riches, under such headings as "Brave and Bold," "Ragged Dick," and "Phil The Fiddler." Over 250 million copies of Horatio Alger books were an inspiration to many boys to make a success of themselves, the writer included. Alger was just over five feet tall, shy, never married, was awkward around women and wrote clumsily about romance. In 1950, Dr. Kenneth Beebe of the American Schools and College Assn. founded the Horatio Alger Awards organization that each year selects 10 awardees, who have been exceptionally successful from humble beginnings. By 1990, there were a total of 250 such recipients, the writer among them, having received the Horatio Alger award in 1979. 381

Rev. William McGuffey

He got $1000 for compiling "McGuffy's Readers" that taught reading, writing, arithmatic and rightousness during last half of 19th century.

Reverend William Holmes McGuffey was paid $1000 for three years work (1834 to 1837) to compile his "Eclectic" readers that sold over 100 million copies during the next 50 years. They were the standard grade school books during the last half of the 19th century that taught righteousness, as well as reading, writing and arithmetic. Iowa schools were among the last to abandon the use of McGuffey readers in 1910. 382

Early settlers used skim milk for paint.

Red Barns – In the early days of America, farmers mixed their own barn paint, and the usual ingredients were iron oxide, skim milk, lime and linseed oil – all this providing a coating that hardened quickly and lasted many years. Georgia clay, which is mostly iron oxide, produced the red color. Even after all colors of paint became available red remained predominant because of tradition (plus the fact that it provided warmth in winter, because it absorbed the sun's rays). 383

Dave Drum, who started KOA campgrounds, never slept in one.

The first KOA (Kamp Grounds of America) was opened by Dave Drum on the banks of the Yellowstone River at Billings, Montana in 1962. This was the original camp ground chain, conceived by Drum, who "never put a dime" of his own money in it and never slept in one. – *from Life 9-29-72* 384

Silo with continuous opening front.

The first upright wooden silo is said to have been built by Fred Hatch, in McHenry County, Illinois in 1873. 385

The first escalator was built as a joy ride on Coney Island.

In 1894 Jesse Reno built the first escalator on the Coney Island New York Pier as a joy ride. It consisted of a conveyor belt pulling an articulated ramp at an angle of 30°, vertically. Seigel Cooper saw it and had four of them installed in their Manhattan department store in 1896. In 1911, London's underground rail system installed an 80 foot rise, the world's highest, and that same year Reno sold his company to the Otis Elevator Company. 386

The British burned the White House in 1814.

The White House got its name after the British burned it in 1814 and the marks of the fire were covered over with white paint. 387

Sheraton Hotel originated in 1939. After World War I, George B. Henderson teamed up with his brother Ernest in a family brokerage firm in Boston. With Ernest's former Harvard roommate, Robert Moore, the brothers began acquiring New England real estate during the early '30s, and in 1937 they bought their first hotel. Two years later they acquired the Boston Sheraton, named after the 18th century English furniture designer; because the hotel's electric rooftop sign was so expensive to remove they adopted the Sheraton name that identified more than 200 hotels around the world in 1975. 388

HAROLD WARP
PIONEER VILLAGE
Minden, Neb. 68959 FOUNDATION

MOTEL was devised by Arthur S. Heineman in 1925, when he coined the word from MOtor hoTEL, for his Milestone Motel halfway between Los Angeles and San Francisco. It was still renting out rooms in 1974. 389

HAROLD WARP
PIONEER VILLAGE
Minden, Neb. 68959 FOUNDATION

The Pronghorn is not really an antelope and is the only hooved animal that originated in North America.

Pronghorns – One of the fleetest animals in the New World, the pronghorn is also one of the rarest. This graceful animal is the only hooved mammal that originated here on the North American continent. Other hooved animals migrated to this country in prehistoric times across the land bridge of the Bering Strait, or, as in the case of the horse, were brought here by man. Actually, the pronghorned antelope is not an antelope, even though it resembles one. It shows certain traits of deer and cattle. The distinct horns of the pronghorn are shed each autumn. A peculiar trait of the pronghorn is the long white hair on their buttocks. By erecting these hairs in the sunlight, these animals can flash brilliant white signals of danger to other members as far away as several miles. Running as fast as 40 miles per hour, as many as 40 million pronghorns populated the western plains, in the days before Indians had horses, wildlife experts estimate. By 1910 their bands were so small and scattered that only emergency protective measures spared them from becoming extinct. 390

500 Fascinating Facts

ANIMALS	Speeds M.P.H.	Gestation Days	Life Years
Ass (Mongolian wild)	40	365	24
Bear (Grizzly)	30	225	31
Cat (domestic)	30	63	15
Coyote	43	61	16
Deer (White-tailed)	30	201	17
Dog (Cape hunting)	45	61	16
Elephant	25	645	47
Elk	45	250	22
Giraffe	32	425	10
Gray fox	42	52	8
Greyhound	39.35	61	16
Horse (Quarter)	47.5	330	27
Lion	50	100	15-29
Man	27.89	270	70
Mouse	6	21	4
Mule deer	35	201	17
Pig (domestic)	11	112	14
Rabbit (domestic)	35	37	5
Rat	8	21	4
Reindeer	32	201	17
Squirrel	12	44	8
Wart hog	30	112	14
Whale	25	365	40-70
Zebra	40	365	20

Man is the longest living land animal.

Most maximum speeds are for quarter mile distance.

391

HAROLD WARP
PIONEER VILLAGE
Minden, Neb. 68959 FOUNDATION

BIRDS	Speeds M.P.H.	Incubation Days	Life Years
Blackbird			12-18
Canary			20-24
Chicken	9	21	12-15
Crow	30-60		
Dove			60-70
Duck	55-70	30	
Eagle (Golden)	120		100-120
Falcon			150-160
Goose (wild)	50-60		50-55
Gull			40-45
Heron			50-60
Humming Bird	55		

Parrots have been known to live over 200 years.

392

147

500 Fascinating Facts

BIRDS	Speeds M.P.H.	Incubation Days	Life Years
Ostrich			60-70
Parrot			200-300
Pheasant	60		
Pigeon	15	18	15-16
Quail	48-58		
Raven			200-300
Swan			100-110
Turkey	50	26	25
Vulture			100-120

The Raven (crow) can live over 200 years.

Most maximum speeds are for quarter mile distance.   393

The fastest living creature is the Spine Tailed Swift. It can fly 106 miles per hour. The minimum speed necessary to place a vehicle in orbit is 18,000 miles per hour.   394

On Columbus's second voyage to America he brought along a few Moorish cattle from Spain that increased to 80,000 Longhorns when Texas became a state in 1836.

Christopher Columbus brought with him from Spain on his second voyage to America in 1493 some hardy, long horned Moorish cattle from Spain's Andalusian plains and dropped them off at Santo Domingo, in the West Indies. From there they were taken to Mexico and a half century later Coronado heading north in search of the Seven Cities of Cibola, drove 500 head across the Rio Grande for food along the way. Thus, this bony, sure footed critter that could live on prickly pear and very little water, acclimated itself naturally to the Texas range. By the time the Lone Star State won its independence in 1836 there were 80,000 longhorns running wild – more critters than humans. Valued at $6 on the hoof in Texas, they brought $40 in Chicago.   395

500 Fascinating Facts

FOUND IN THE NEW WORLD	BROUGHT FROM THE OLD WORLD
Corn	Horse
Potato	Cattle
Tomato	Pig
Peppers	Sheep
(Bell and Chili)	Chicken
Chocolate	Pheasant
Cocoa	Honeybee
Vanilla	Sparrow, Starling
Tobacco	Wheat, Asian Rice,
Beans	Barley, Oats,
(Lima, Pole,	Soy Beans
Navy, Kidney)	Sugar Cane
Pumpkin	Onion
Cassova Root	Lettuce
(Manioc)	Okra
Avocodo	Peach and Pear
Peanut, Pecan,	Watermelon
Cashew	Citrus Fruit
Pineapple	Banana
Blueberry	Olive
Sunflower	Lilac
Petunia	Daffodil
Black-Eyed Susan	Tulip
Dahlia	Daisy
Marigold	Dandelion
Quinine	Crab Grass
Wild Rice	Turnips
Squash	Beets
Turkey	
Bison	
Antelope	396

Corn and potatoes were found in America. Horses and cattle came from the old country.

Maverick – It has come to mean an unorthodox, "lone wolf" type of person. Originally, it meant an unbranded calf. It comes from Samuel A. Maverick, a Texas rancher who didn't brand his cattle. 397

An unbranded calf was a Maverick.

States that have Indian Names

Half of all the names of this nation's states are Indian in origin. Here are some examples:

Alabama – Creek Indian word meaning "Here we rest."

Arizona – Indian word meaning "Place of small springs."

Arkansas – Quapaw Indian Tribe.

Connecticut – Indian word meaning beside or on the long river.

Dakota – Indian name for "allies."

Idaho – Shoshone Indian word E-Dah-Ho, meaning "Behold! the sun coming down the mountain."

Illinois – Indian word "Illini" meaning "A great man."

Most of our states have Indian names.

Iowa – Indian name meaning "Sleepy waters."

Kansas – Kaw Indian tribe meaning "Wind people."

Kentucky – Indian name "Kentake" meaning "Prairie."

Massachusetts – Indian word meaning "Great Hills."

Michigan – Indian name for "Great Lake."

Minnesota – Indian name meaning "Cloud-tinted waters."

Mississippi – Indian words meaning "Great river."

Missouri – Missouri tribe meaning "Town of the large canoes."

Nebraska – Otoe Indian name meaning "Fat Water."

Ohio – Indian name for "Beautiful river."

Oklahoma – Choctaw Indian word meaning "Red people."

Texas – Indian word "Tejas" meaning "Friends or Allies."

Wisconsin – Indian name meaning "Meeting of the rivers."

– Liguorian

398

HAROLD WARP
PIONEER VILLAGE
Minden, Neb. 68959 FOUNDATION

Any jackass can kick a barn down, but it takes a carpenter to build one.

399

When asked what that funny animal was, the Aboriginese answered Gong-ga-roo, meaning "I don't know".

The word "Kangaroo" is aboriginal, meaning "I don't know" as related by Australian guide Quentin Smith. When Englishmen first came to Australia, one of them asked what that funny animal was and the Aborigine answered "Gong-ga-roo" which means "I don't know."   400

Before Christ was born the Chinese were using powdered Chrysanthemums to kill fleas.

The Chinese made the first insecticide in the first century B.C. using dried, powdered chrysanthemums to kill fleas, according to *The World Almanac Book of Inventions* by Valerie-Anne Giscard d'Estaing. This insecticide, called pyrethrum, gained popularity in Europe in the 18th century and is widely used today in both dust and spray forms because it rapidly kills flying insects with little effect on humans and domestic animals. To be effective, pyrethrum must come into contact with the flying insect.   401

It took Erick Rotheim 15 years to convince someone to make his insect spray can.

In 1926 Erick Rotheim, Norwegian engineer, patented a liquid such as Freon or Butane that would turn to a gas below approximately 10 lbs. pressure, mixed with a product that could be propelled from a can into a fine spray. Rotheim had trouble selling his idea and the first to use it commercially in 1941 were two American chemists, Goodhue and Sullivan, who produced the first insect spray in an aerosol can that year.   402

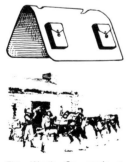

The Wyeth Co. made a Mochilla for Mr. Warp in 1961, from the same patterns they used 100 years earlier.

In 1961 Mr. Warner, of the Wyeth Hardware Company of St. Joseph, Missouri agreed to make a Pony Express mail carrying Mochilla for Harold Warp, to go with the Pony Express Station he had purchased for his Pioneer Village at Minden, Nebraska. Wyeth used the same patterns that they had used 100 years before when they made the mochillas for Majors and Waddell.   403

Although an American named Wright obtained a patent in England in 1824 on the common pin, it was not until 1836 that John Howe perfected a machine and started making pins in Derby, Connecticut. Today every man, woman and child in the United States uses an average of 125 pins per year and approximately 99% of them are lost and return to the soil. 404

John Howe made the first common pin in the U.S. in 1836.

Safety pins were developed by Wm. Hunt and patented by him on April 10, 1849; little did he realize that they would become popular world wide, and still be in use more than 100 years later. Millions are sold annually, yet he sold his patent for $200 when the public at first refused to accept the safety pin. 405

Wm. Hunt patented the safety pin in 1849.

It made the man a millionaire who though of putting the crimp in the common hairpin. 406

One day in 1903, when Albert J. Parkhouse returned to work at this Timberlake Wire and Novelty Co. in Jackson, Michigan, all the coat hooks were taken, so Parkhouse proceeded to bend a wire into his coat's width shape, with a hook at the top, that he hung on the cupboard door knob. When his employer saw the wire coat hanger, he immediately seized the idea and patented it. Parkhouse continued to work at the factory and received nothing for his idea. 407

Albert Parkhouse, who bent up the first wire coat hanger in 1903, never bothered to patent it.

The first pencil with an attached eraser was patented in 1858. 408

Africa's Sahara Desert covers three and a half million square miles, 16 times more area than France. 409

Boycott – In 1880, Captain Charles Boycott, a landlord's agent in an Irish village, refused to accept lower rents during hard times. The tenants combined to have no dealings of any kind with him, and his name has since become a synonym for ostracism. 410

Some highlights in Stock Exchange history: Adoption in 1863 of the name "New York Stock Exchange"; installation in 1867 of the first stock tickers; making memberships saleable in 1868; establishment in 1871 of a continuous auction market to replace the call market; installation in 1879 of the first telephones; and recording the first one-million share day in 1886. 411

Fire-Crackers became popular for celebrating Independence Day after the Civil War. Previous to that time bells were rung on the 4th of July. 412

South of the Equator all climbing vines twine from right to left. North of the Equator they twine from left to right. 413

Roller skates were invented by Joseph Merlin of London in 1760. 414

The Washington-head, 25-cent piece went into circulation on August 1, 1932. 415

BOBBY – This term for a London policeman came from the nickname of the British statesman Sir Robert Peel, who organized the city's police force in 1829. 416

Mackintosh – This type of raincoat is named for Charles Mackintosh, a Scottish inventor and chemist who developed a waterproof fabric as a result of his search for a way of using waste products from the manufacture of coal gas for lighting. 417

Coal gas by-products water proofed the raincoat made by Charles Mackintosh.

Tennessee Warbler was named by Alexander Wilson, Scottish born ornithologist, who published eight volumes on American birds before John James Audubon. While visiting in Tennessee Wilson noticed a warbler that nested in Canada, in the early 1800s. 418

A Scotchman named the Tennessee Warbler.

British farmers had long observed that cows often developed lesions on their udders – a disease known as cowpox – and that those who milked the cows and developed similar-appearing lesions on their hands never contracted smallpox. In 1774, Benjamin Jesty, a Dorset dairy farmer, inoculated his wife and two children during a local smallpox outbreak by scratching fluid from a cowpox lesion into their skin. The inoculations were successful; the fluid apparently caused the production of antibodies against smallpox. Then, in 1796, Edward Jenner, a Gloucestershire physician, inoculated an eight-year-old boy with cowpox fluid and, seven weeks later, variolated the boy with material from a smallpox lesion. The subject did not develop smallpox. Jenner referred to his experiment as vaccination – from the Latin vaccinus, meaning "pertaining to cow" – and submitted a paper on it to the Royal Society of England, which rejected it. He consequently had the paper published at his own expense, which resulted in the practice of vaccination. Smallpox vaccine used today is produced by inoculating calves with a virus similar to smallpox and then collecting the material from the subsequent lesions on the calves' skin. – *Gleaned from 9-75 Natural History* 419

Smallpox vaccine was discovered by a British farmer in 1774, while milking his cows. Even the Latin word vaccinus means "pertaining to a cow".

A willow sprout was planted in a tub of earth and nothing added for five years except water. At the end of that time, the plant weighed 164 pounds and the dirt in the tub had decreased only two ounces. 420

Sunshine and water goes into a tree, not the soil.

Minden, Neb. 68959

After taking a quart of blood two sucessive days from George Washington, with an instrument like this, the third day, shortly before noon he died December 14, 1799; he calmly said "I die hard".

Did you know that the single blade bleeder was called the "George Washington Bleeder"? He had laryngitis and the doctor said, "he has bad blood – we've got to bleed him," so they took a quart of blood. The next day Washington still was no better, so they bled him again and the third day he died, December 14, 1799. Shortly before passing away Washington calmly stated, "I die hard." Today they would have given him new blood instead of taking it away from him. Blood-letting or phlebotomy was the common relief for inflammatory diseases for centuries. It was even resorted to in the spring and fall as a hygienic precaution. 421

Minden, Neb. 68959

One day in 1815, a young physician, Rene' Laennee got the idea for a stethoscope while watching children scrape the one end of a fallen tree trunk, while children at the other end of the tree trunk heard the scraping noise loud and clear by putting their ear to the tree. Laennee proceeded to make a wooden tube 10 inches long and 3/4" across. By placing one end of the tube against a patient's chest, and the other against his ear, he could hear heartbeats and also the flow of air in and out of the lungs. Wooden stethoscopes continued to be used until 1913, when a Chicago druggist, "Doc" Fleisher, 31 years of age, invented the rubber diaphragm stethoscope, still being used in 1990. 422

"Doc" Fleisher

Children playing on a hollow tree in 1815 spearked the stethoscope.

Minden, Neb. 68959

On death, arteries empty themselves. Finding them empty, ancient anatomists thought they were air passages, and so the word artery derived from the Latin for windpipe. 423

The word thermometer means heat measure in Greek.

FAHRENHEIT – Gabriel Daniel Fahrenheit (1686-1736), a German physicist, developed the thermometer scale that bears his name. By using mercury instead of alcohol in the tube, he made it more accurate than those in use earlier. The word "thermometer" comes from the Greek word meaning "heat measure".   424

Andrew Hamilton, a Philadelphia lawyer, won the first "freedom of the press" case for a jailed New York publisher, when New York lawyers were afraid to defend him.

Everyone has heard the term, "Philadelphia lawyer", but not everyone knows how the expression was born. Back in 1734 and 1735, when Peter Zenger was jailed in New York for publishing a newspaper that criticized the colonial government, all the New York lawyers were afraid to touch the defense of Zenger. Andrew Hamilton, a Philadelphia lawyer, took the case and won the country's first legal victory for freedom of the press. That is how the term "Philadelphia lawyer" got into the language.   425

Until 1880 there were fifty different standard times in use in the United States, though nobody had ever heard of daylight saving time.   426

BRAILLE – In 1829 a French teacher of the blind, Louis Braille, invented this system of printing and writing, in which characters are represented by raised dots – a development of immeasurable value to those suffering from blindness.   427

The first ball game was played at Hoboken, N.J. 6/19/1846, similar to a game Indians played.

BASEBALL, as we know it today was first played in Hoboken, New Jersey June 19, 1846, between New York Knickerbockers and the New York Club. Rules developed were: nine men on a side, three outs and a diamond with bases 90 feet apart.   428

Clement Moore's 1822 poem, "Twas the Night Before Christmas", made the REINDEER a part of our Christmas tradition. 429

Millions of children learned to spell using Noah Webster's "Blue Back" book of words.

Blue-Back Spellers by Noah Webster helped set a standard for spelling in our country. Millions of children learned to spell using his book. He lived from 1758 to 1843. 430

The first Ferris Wheel was built by George Ferris for the World's Columbian Exposition in 1893. 431

The original "Mills" slot machine was a long wooden trough that pennies could roll down. When a penny was rolled into a certain can at the bottom of the chute the "gambler" collected. The law of averages prevailed then, as it does today. Mr. Mills took his contraption to carnivals and fairs in the early 1900s and from it the slot machine evolved. 432

Goodyear discovered how to vulcanize rubber when he had an accident on a hot stove.

In 1844 Ellsworth Goodyear accidentally dropped a mixture of sulphur and rubber latex on a hot stove and thus discovered how to vulcanize rubber. It was first used for pneumatic bicycle tires in 1890. In the early 1900s the life of automobile tires was increased considerably by the addition of carbon black, which cut down the destructive action of the sun's rays. The carbon black did not allow these rays to penetrate into the tire, leaving a minute layer of decomposed rubber on the exposed surface. That is why you sometimes get a black smudge on your finger when you touch a tire. Although rubber is not commonly considered a plastic, it was the forerunner of many of our modern plastics today. 433

The first thing made of Goodyear's vulcanized rubber was rubber footwear.

Ellsworth Goodyear discovered how to vulcanize rubber when he patented the process in 1844. The first to use Goodyear's vulcanized rubber patent was C.L. Candee of Hampton, Connecticut, who made the first footwear using Goodyear's vulcanized rubber patent. 434

The "Surrey with the Fringe on the Top" was responsible for the pneumatic tire. In 1896 Alexander Winton asked B.F. Goodrich to make him a set of air inflated tires for his Winton car, similar to what he had seen on a carriage in 1895. Mr. Goodrich made Mr. Winton pay for the dies to make the tires, because Mr. Goodrich didn't think there would ever be enough demand for air inflated tires to pay for the dies himself. See the "Surrey with the Fringe on Top" that inspired the first air filled auto tires at Harold Warp Pioneer Village Foundation at Minden in south central Nebraska. 435

The surry "with the fringe on top" inspired the first car tires.

Goodrich made Mr. Winton pay for the dies to make the first pneumatic tire put on a car in 1896.

Prior to 1910 auto tires had smooth surfaces that caused the car to slide all over the road in rainy weather, causing the tires to more easily pick up nails buried in the mud that had shaken loose from hay racks and lumber wagons. The life of those early auto tires was approximately 1000 miles. Every car carried a jack, wrenches and tire patching supplies for "flat tires". Tires were white because white lead was added to the rubber to keep the sun's actinic rays from penetrating the rubber and ruining the tire. Lamp black is currently used as a sun-block on black tires. 436

Early cars had smooth white tires that slid all over in mud and were good for only 1000 miles.

Firestone put "non-skip" tires on Fords in 1914.

The first patent on a "mutilated" auto tire with notched tread was taken out in 1903 by Alvaro S. Krotz. He later sold his patent to the Kelly Springfield Tire Company, but it was 1914 when Firestone introduced the first "non-skid" wording

Sears sold a "motor buggy" from 1906 until 1912.

The smooth tires on horseless carriages took folks nowhere without tire chains when it rained.

on the face of Ford tires at a 45° angle, spaced 1½" apart. Krotz also designed the first storage battery for the Willard Storage Battery Company in 1901. He also designed and built the Sears Motor Buggy in 1906 that Sears carried in their catalog until 1912, when Sears sold it to the Lincoln Motor Car Company.   437

First Pneumatic Tire – B.F. Goodrich, 1895
First Clincher Tire – Harvey Firestone, 1899
First Tire Chains – Harry D. Weed, N.Y., 1904
First Cord Tire – B.F. Goodrich, 1910
First Demountable Tire – Louis H. Pearman, 1913
First Non-Skid Tire – Stacy C. Fiesta, 1914
First Balloon Tire – Firestone, 1923
First Butadiene Tire – B.F. Goodrich, 1940
First Tubeless Tire – B.F. Goodrich, 1947   438

Automobile Tire Chains - 1904 – There had been several attempts to fasten some kind of contraption to car wheels, or to the rubber tires, that were all made with smooth surfaces in those days, to prevent the tires from spinning on ice, snow or mud. The problem was solved when Harry Parsons, an Englishman, patented the first automobile tire chain in the U.S. on August 23, 1904, that did not fasten to the tire or to the wheel. He gave the Weed Company of Bridgeport, Connecticut the U.S. rights to his patent that same year, 1904.

For many years thereafter every car carried with it a pair of Weed Tire Chains. Some manufacturers even furnished a pair of Weed Tire Chains with the car, until Harvey Firestone commenced putting "non-skid" in raised letters diagonally across the face of the tire in 1914. Other tire makers soon followed suit, by putting some design on the face of their tires, (in recent years truly a skid-proof design), and the smooth faced tire, thankfully, became a thing of the past.   439

Styrene Polymers

Even yachts are made of Styrene Syrup over fiberglass.

The basic raw materials for making styrene is ethylene and benzine, discovered by Simon in 1839. It did not come into general use, however, until World War II when it was used for making tires, when rubber became unavailable for civilian use. Polymerized styrene is a clear, hard plastic. Mouldable into toys, drinking glasses, etc., when mixed with certain chemicals it becomes "Styrofoam". Used as a syrup for fiberglass, this combination can be moulded into a myriad of items, including auto bodies and boat hulls. 440

Carl Fisher started canning the liquid they were dumping in the river and called it Prestone.

In making Carl Fisher's Pres-O-Lite the residue was poured in the White River at Indianapolis. As time went on it was noticed the river did not freeze where the liquid residue was being dumped in so it was put in one gallon cans and sold as "Prestone" antifreeze for automobiles. 441

Leo Baekeland was trying to find a substitute for the Indian lac bug juice when he discovered "Bakelite".

In 1909, Leo Henrich Baekeland, while trying to find a substitute for shellac, which was then made from the juice of the Indian lac bug, mixed up a batch of phenol, formaldehyde and alkali that hardened into an amber colored, non-burning solid, which he later found had excellent electrical insulating properties. He named it "bakelite". One of its first uses was for amber pipe stems, later for electrical parts on automobiles. The complete development of plastics can be seen at the Harold Warp Pioneer Village, Minden, Nebraska. 442

Harold Warp

Sometimes it pays to quit for the night.

The formula for Flex-O-Glass was discovered by Harold Warp in 1924 when he left an experimental mixture on a cook stove overnight and when he heated up the stove the next morning the mixture had congealed. 443

When an insect screening with clear plastic strands of monofilament was conceived by Harold Warp in 1938, he went to a man in Chicago who was extruding toothbrush bristles. Mr. Warp asked him if he would extrude some clear monofilament of Warp's own formula. The man told Mr. Warp he could have the continuous monofilament strands, but they had to be just like those going into the barrel. Mr. Warp took a barrel full of the red strands, figuring he could at least find out if the plastic could be properly woven. That was why the very first plastic insect screen ever woven was colored red.　　444

Red was an odd color for the first plastic fly screen.

HAROLD WARP
PIONEER VILLAGE FOUNDATION
Minden, Neb. 68959

When a U.S. Patent application for plastic window screen was filed by Harold Warp in 1940, a patent was denied him. The U.S. Patent office claimed plastic was merely a substitute for metal insect screening. Several years later, one of Warp's competitors, Mr. Rigenstein had noticed there was no patent on plastic insect screen and somehow he was able to obtain a patent. Mr. Warp could have proved in court that he had previously applied for a U.S. patent that was denied him. The simplest and less costly procedure was to agree to pay Mr. Rigenstein a royalty of $1 a year for the 17 year life of his patent, as suggested by Mr. Warp, which was done.　　445

A simple way to solve a sad situation.

HAROLD WARP
PIONEER VILLAGE FOUNDATION
Minden, Neb. 68959

Jiffy-WRAP is the ORIGINAL Polyethylene Plastic Food Wrap

His grocers could find no room on their shelves for Warp's first polyethylene food wrap and garbage bags.

Clear Plastic UTILITY SIZE Bags — JIFFIES

When the first polyethylene plastic food wrap "Jiffy Wrap" was developed by Harold Warp, and also the first plastic garbage bags, his local grocers would not try to sell them, claiming they had no room on their shelves for untried items. It was several months before Warp's salesman received an order for these items. The (Star) grocery chain in Minneapolis gave Warp the first order for his Jiffy Wrap. The first store to try Warp's polyethylene garbage bags was a grocery store in Highland Park, Illinois. It didn't take long for Union Carbide to come out with Glad Wrap and Glad Bags, and Dow with Handy Wrap, but it took them years to discover the cling features of Warp's "Jiffy Wrap".　　446

Gutsa-Percha ink stand.

Shellac button molding press.

Cases made from molded shellac (juice of lac bug).

Origin of the Plastics Industry, 1843-1963 – For centuries the Malayans have used the sap of the percha tree, gutta-percha, a semi-elastic gum, for knife handles and other useful articles. Their method of molding was crude, but effective. They merely softened the material in hot water and shaped it by hand. A surgeon in Malaya, Dr. Montgomerie, returned to England in 1843 with this information and the Gutta-Percha Company evolved, that rolled it into sheets for surgeons' splints and they also molded such things as ink stands and billiard balls in die molds, using hand screw presses. (This was 30 years before Hyatt discovered cellulose nitrate for billiard balls.) Michael Faraday, an English chemist who was fooling with electricity, discovered that gutta-percha was a good insulator, especially so under water, which opened up a new field, insulation in ocean cable, and the company continued in business until 1930.

In 1843 Alfred Critchlow, an Englishman who fashioned buttons and combs from horns, migrated to the United States and settled in Haydenville, Massachusetts, where he discovered that the juices of the lac bug (shellac) could be molded into various objects in a compression press. By 1850 he had several customers who made buttons, checkers, picture frames, etc., from his lac gum. Among Critchlow's customers were Samuel Peck of New Haven and Halor Halvorson of Boston, who molded daguerreotype cases. In 1853 Alfred Critchlow commenced molding them himself, in Florence, Massachusetts and was soon running two 12-hour shifts. The company he founded is the Prophylactic Brush Company.

The first machine for extruding gutta-percha into tubes was invented by H. Bewley in 1845, which opened up an entirely new concept in continuous production, as science later concocted plastics capable of extrusion. In the meantime, in 1844, Ellsworth Goodyear accidentally dropped a mixture of rubber and sulphur on a hot stove and thus discovered how to vulcanize rubber. As time went on india-rubber gradually replaced the less flexible and less versatile gutta-percha in many applications.

An Albany, New York printer, John Wesley Hyatt,

should not be credited with discovering cellulose nitrate, but he should be given credit for making it commercially feasible. He was attracted by a $10,000 offer of Phelan and Collander seeking a substitute for gutta-percha and ivory in the manufacture of their billiard balls. Several years after reading their offer and eight patents later, Hyatt's patent dated July 12, 1870, describing a "unique and critical action of camphor on cellulose nitrate" won him the $10,000 award and sparked our plastics industry, although it could not be molded. Solvents had to be evaporated from it to form a sheet and sheets had to be laminated together to form a block. He called it Celluloid. Celluloid continued to be made until 1950, when the trade mark was dropped by the Celanese Company. Every carriage and automobile at one time had celluloid (nitro-cellulose) side curtains, commonly called "Isinglass" in error. Celluloid shirt collars were also the vogue in the early 1900s.

India rubber mold.

Prior to Hyatt's 1870 Celluloid patent, J. Pelouze had, in 1835, dissolved wood fiber, paper and rags in nitric acid. Ten years later a Swiss chemist, Schoenbein, nitrated cellulose by using sulphuric acid instead of nitric acid. In 1854 a patent was granted J. Cutting of Boston who had discovered "gum camphor in collodion (cellulose nitrate) improves the quality of photographs," but he did not follow through on his discovery. In 1862 Alexander Parks exhibited "Parkesine" at the International Exhibition in London in the form of buttons, combs, and knife handles, describing it as "a hard, horny, elastic, weatherproof substance left after evaporation of the solvent of collodion" (cellulose nitrate in ether/alcohol), but he failed to include the camphor that was responsible for the success of Hyatt's formula eight years later.

Parkesine Plaque.

Leo Hendrich Baekeland, born in Belgium in 1863, a science and electro-chemistry teacher in Germany, migrated to America in 1889. He invented "Velox" photopaper. He sold it to George Eastman for one million dollars in 1900. He opened an office in Yonkers, New York, as a consulting research chemist. At that time the molded product market was served by rubber, natural bitumen (grahamite, etc.) and shellac. (The new wonder plastic

Bakelite Insulators.

"celluloid" could be formed but could not be molded.) While Mr. Baekeland was searching for a synthetic shellac (the juice of the Indian lac bug), he came up with a non-burning, amber colored, insulating resin by mixing phenol, formaldehyde and alkali. He announced his invention as "Bakelite" in 1909. It had good insulating properties. Many insulating parts were subsequently molded of it in the new electrical field, as well as pipe stems and small gears. Hemp or burlap was a good "filler" material.

Mr. Seabury mixed in with Baekeland's synthetic varnish (which was a substitute for lac bug juice) some asbestos and some wood flour, in 1907. He molded this into a rubber substitute for electrical insulators to produce Mr. Baekeland's first Bakelite.

Richard W. Seabury, founder of the Boonton Rubber Company, later to become Tech-Art Plastics Company, is credited as being the first molder of Bakelite. Here is Mr. Seabury's account of how it happened: "In 1906 I was running a small plant in Boonton, New Jersey, called Loando hard Rubber Company. About this time, the Vulcanized Rubber Company in Trenton wanted us to reduce the inorganic material in our 'Loando' rubber. We consulted a chemist, Dr. Leo Henrich Baekeland of Yonkers, New York, who was working on a phenolic resin. Whereas Baekeland was interested in a synthetic varnish, I was interested in the resin itself as a substitute for rubber in molded electrical insulation compounds. The first molded Bakelite parts, some filled with asbestos and others with woodflour, were made by me in 1907. Dr. Baekeland brought the resin from his Yonkers laboratory and I made the molding powders and molded the parts in our molds and presses. My first customer for this new 'Bakelite' material was the Weston Electrical Instrument Corporation."

Warp's Flex-O-Glass let the sun's ultra-violet rays through chicken house windows to keep young chicks from dying.

During World War I Dreyfuss Brothers developed a dope for airplane wings using acetic acid, that withstood sunlight better than nitro-cellulose and it could be made non-combustible. They called it Cellulose Acetate, which became widely used for movies and photofilm in the 1930s. In 1924 an inexpensive substitute for window glass was introduced by Harold Warp, that would admit ultra-violet rays from the sun, then stopped by common glass. It was a French talc, stearate and wax impregnated fabric. He called it Flex-O-Glass. In 1925 DuPont introduced Cellophane to replace wrapping paper consisting of cellulose cut in acids.

In 1935 DuPont made celophane semi-moisture proof by sealing two layers together with a layer of wax. In 1927 Kienle patented thermosetting Alkyd Resin, glyceryl, phthalate and drying oils. The name was coined by AL for alcohol and KYD for acid. In 1932 Clark and Malm patented transparent weather-resistant Butyrate (cellulose cut in butyric and acetic acids), and that same year Union Carbide, who had bought out Baekeland's Bakelite, announced a clear thermoplastic Vinylite (the residue that accumulated in the manufacture of "Prest-O-Lite" and "Prestone".) In 1936 Rohm and Haas introduced a clear acrylic resin, Plexiglass, made from acrylic acids and their derivitives, and that same year Dr. W.H. Carothers discovered Nylon in his DuPont laboratory. He committed suicide shortly after his discovery and did not live to see Nylon in production. Polyethylene was developed in 1942 by Imperial Chemical Company of England and was first made in the U.S. in 1943, primarily for war purposes. In 1942, when the Japanese cut off our supply of rubber from the Far East, the U.S. Government financed plants to make synthetic rubber (butadyene) from a synthetic latex discovered by Simon in 1839, that he called "Styrol." After World War II, when rubber again became available this ethylene-benzine base was polymerized into a hard, clear resin (Styrene), which has a tendency to break down when exposed to ultra-violet light, widely used as a syrup to make stiff fiberglass forms and sheets.

Union Carbide Co. discovered that the gummy resinous residue from making Prestone anti-freeze could be formed into a plastic that they named Vinylite.

In 1946 H. Warp introduced a clear, flexible window material to replace his cloth base Flex-O-Glass of 1924. It consisted of acraloid, vinyl chloride, trichrysol phosphate and dibutyl phthylate, cut in solvents of ketone and acetone. It was cast on a highly polished moving metal belt, did not stop the sun's heathful actinic rays, yet was guaranteed to last for years as a window. Since 1950 so many cross-blends, concoctions and innovations have taken place in the plastics field, such as "ABS" (a combination of Acrylonitrile, Butadyene, and Styrene), that we are no longer able to keep up with them. – *H. Warp; Portions by J.H. DuBois*   447

Warp's new Flex-O-Glass was crystal clear and long lasting.

While searching for a substitute for Ivory for billiard balls, Hyatt brothers discovered clear "Celluloid" that became widely used as touring car windows and men's collars.

Celluloid, 1900 – In 1869 the Hyatt brothers, while searching for something to replace elephant tusk ivory, patented a mixture of gum camphor mixed with gun-cotton dissolved in nitric acid to produce the first practical nitrocellulose plastic material. They called it Celluloid. It became widely used in the late 1800s for piano keys and billiard balls, for side curtain windows in buggies, carriages, and later in cars, as well as a base for metal paints. It was highly inflammable and like rubber, could not withstand the destructive force of the sun's actinic rays unless highly pigmented. It finally went down in history in favor of more durable and more versatile plastics, since developed. Ironically, the trademark was dropped in 1950. (The business that celluloid built became the "Celanese Corporation.")   448

Dr. Baekeland, while searching for a substitute for the juice of the lac bug (shellac), discovered Bakelite.

Bakelite, 1909 – Dr. Leo Baekeland was trying to make shellac synthetically when he came up with something entirely different in 1889. (The Indian lac bug, from which shellac was made, has never been duplicated synthetically.) In 1909 Baekeland received the Nichols Medal of the American Chemical Society for inventing a mixture of phenol, formaldehyde and alkali, to make "Bakelite" a non-burning, high insulating, tough amber colored thermo-setting resin. It replaced rubber, celluloid and ivory in many items, and has, when saturated with hemp or burlap, since replaced metal in many machined parts. Most persons remember seeing Bakelite for the first time in the amber colored pipe stems of Meerschaum pipes along about 1910 and thereafter. As the years went by the uses for this type of resin multiplied, until by 1950 it vied for first place with vinyl. 463 million pounds were produced in 1951. – *The original non-melting (thermo-setting) Bakelite should not be confused with its present offspring, the Bakelite Company, which specializes in meltable resins.*   449

The original translucent Flex-O-Glass of the 1920s and 1930s should not be confused with present day Crystal Clear Flex-O-Glass, now widely used for windows and coverings and sold in hardware stores everywhere. In 1924 Harold Warp patented a French-talc treated cloth impregnated with a stearate-wax composition, to make the first practical weatherproof ultra-violet transmitting substitute for glass, commercially. It was used in poultry and brooder house windows, etc., to obtain natural benefits from the sun's rays, to prevent rickets in chicks and pigs, and also to increase egg production. Common glass stopped these beneficial rays of the sun. Flex-O-Glass could be made so inexpensively that folks by the millions used it, not only for poultry house windows, but also for winter protection in their homes, where it could easily be tacked over windows. It was always sold on a two year, money back guarantee. It was replaced by a crystal clear Flex-O-Glass in 1946. 450

When Warp first advertised his Flex-O-Glass to "make the sun work for you" the sun's ultra-violet rays had not yet been acknowledged.

HAROLD WARP PIONEER VILLAGE FOUNDATION
Minden, Neb. 68959

Cellophane, 1925 – Cellophane, a tissue thin colorless slow burning plastic, (patented by Brandenberger in 1912), and produced by DuPont, was introduced about 1925 for wrapping expensive candies, etc. When first introduced it was considered so valuable by candy manufacturers that some kept it in their safes. It commenced to be widely used for wrapping in the 1930s and today almost "everything" comes in Cellophane. Like paper it is not moisture-proof and along about 1935 DuPont discovered that a thin layer of wax on the surface would help hold in moisture, thus two layers could keep popcorn bags, etc., fairly moisture-proof for a period of time. 451

When first introduced folks were afraid Cellophane would explode because it looked like nitrocellulose.

HAROLD WARP PIONEER VILLAGE FOUNDATION
Minden, Neb. 68959

Cellulose Acetate, 1926 – During World War I a dope for the cloth used on airplane wings, that withstood sunlight and weathering better than nitrocellulose, was developed by Dreyfuss and others. It consisted of cellulose, acetic acid and sulphuric acid. During the late 1920s cellulose acetate com-

Cellulose Acetate

It wouldn't burn like the nitrates.

menced to be used to replace silk in the form of "rayon" and it was also proving more desirable for rods, sheets and tubes than the nitrates. In 1939 it became the base for some of Warp's Window Materials, due to its exceptional weathering and high ultra-violet transmission properties. It is still used for this purpose. 97 million pounds were produced in 1951.   452

In 1927 Kienle filed a patent covering the modification of glyceryl phthalate with drying oils, later declared invalid. The name "Alkyd" was coined by Kienle from the combination of "al" for alcohol and "kyd" for acid. The resin is actually formed by a reaction of phthalic anhydride with glycerol. It is a thermosetting resin and its chief uses are for paints and enamels. Production in 1951 was 439,708,908 pounds.   453

Kienle's Alkyd resin patent was claimed invalid.

Vinyl Resin, 1932 – When Fisher started dissolving carbide in his Indianapolis plant and placed the gas derived therefrom in "Prest-O-Lite" tanks so autoists didn't have to fool with carbide, along about 1905, he noticed the White River, where they dumped the liquid residue, did not freeze. Thus they started selling it as "Prestone" to put in radiators to keep cars from freezing up in winter. With the advent of electric auto lights and an increase in the number of "anti-freeze" minded motorists, the Carbide Company had to find a new way to make anti-freeze economically. They found it in natural gas, but a thick, gummy residue was also obtained in making antifreeze. In trying to find a use for this residue, "Vinylite", a tough, colorless, meltable (thermoplastic) resin, was finally put on the market in the early 1930s, (formula developed in Germany.) It has grown to be a very versatile product, widely used in the plastics field.   454

Vinylite was also a chance discovery.

Rohm & Haas promised to vacuum form Plexiglass but did not keep their promise.

Acrylic Resin, 1936 – Chemically formed from acrylic acids, and their derivatives, this thermoplastic formula was developed by Otto Rohm of Germany and it was brought to the United States in 1936. Rohm and Haas have since licensed DuPont to make acrylics and Harold Warp licensed Rohm and Haas to use the name "Plexiglass". Being very light stable (but easily scratched) it gained favor during World War II as vacuum formed windshields in airplanes. It is easily formed when subjected to heat, cuts like wood, and has a peculiar characteristic of carrying light rays through it edgeways; this characteristic was discovered in 1945. 455

Nylon, 1936 – Dr. W.H. Carothers, while trying to duplicate Vinylite, using the base ingredients from which gas is formed (coal, lime and air) discovered and patented Nylon. Nylon is actually a combination of benzol or phenol, oxygen, ammonia, hydrogen and nitrogen, subjected to various heats, pressures and conversions to form giant molecules. It was first synthesized in 1936, was first used for tooth brush bristles in 1938 and first used for women's stockings in 1940. Dr. Carothers never lived to see quantity production of his miraculous oriented filament, for he took his own life on completion of his experiments. It was especially adapted for women's hosiery and for fine fabrics. This polyamide resin has exceptionally high tensile strength when oriented and its use during World War II was restricted to such items as rope, parachutes, etc., before it became available for civilian use after the war. (Orientation is equivalent to freezing a rubber band while it is stretched out.) 456

Nylon – 1936
While trying to duplicate Vinylite for DuPont, Carothers came up with Nylon, but committed suicide before it was made into a pair of hosiery.

The first nylon hosiery went on sale on October 25, 1939. Discovered by Dr. W.H. Carothers in 1936 and patented by DuPont, Carothers committed suicide in 1937, long before the first pair of stockings were made from his invention. 457

Butyrate could be made fire retardent and longer lasting.

Butyrate, 1936 – In 1932 Clark and Malm obtained a patent on a mixture of cellulose, butyric and acetic acids and anhydrides to make cellulose acetate butyrate. It has better outdoor weathering qualities and dimensional stability than acetate and became widely used for tool handles, Warp's Window Materials, airplane dopes, etc.   458

HAROLD WARP
PIONEER VILLAGE
Minden, Neb. 68959 FOUNDATION

Melamine Resin remained dormant for 100 years.

Melamine Resin, 1939 – Although a compound of carbon, nitrogen and hydrogen was first synthesized in the laboratory of Justus Von Leibig in 1834, since known as Melamine, nothing further was done on it until 1939, when it became possible to produce Melamine with complicated equipment operating at high pressure. Melamine is today made from calcium cyanamide by the intermediate production of Dicyanodiamide. It is a thermosetting resin and its chief uses are for restaurant counter tops, table-ware, ignition parts, buttons, plywood adhesive, etc.   459

HAROLD WARP
PIONEER VILLAGE
Minden, Neb. 68959 FOUNDATION

Cheap ethylene gas, mixed with oxygen, at high pressures, produced the first polyethylene.

Polyethylene Resins, 1943 – This resin came out of World War II. It is just what its name implies, polymerized ethylene, developed in Europe and first quantity production undertaken in the United States was in 1943. It is a pliable, waxy, translucent, waterproof material that has the peculiar characteristic of allowing oxygen to pass through it, thus being ideal for packaging certain foods. It can be made from grain and could be instrumental in stabilizing grain prices. Polyethylene is commonly made from ethylene, an inexpensive by-product of natural gas. It was originally produced by subjecting ethylene gas to an extremely high pressure of over 30,000 pounds per square inch, which at the same time elevated the temperature from 300° to 500° F. Under these conditions oxygen acts as a catalyst, causing the short ethylene molecules to link up into long, many-branched giant molecules that emerge from the reacting chamber as a solid plastic. It was first developed by Imperial Chemical Industries, Ltd., following Walter Carother's

Polyethylene has become the most widely used plastic.

brilliant invention of nylon and its giant molecule construction. In 1953 Karl Ziegler, a German chemist, discovered a method of producing polyethylene without subjecting the gas to such extreme pressures, but by using organometals instead, such as triethyl aluminum in combination with titanium tetrachloride, dispersed in a hydrocarbon solvent, to which the ethylene was added, causing the mixture to immediately polymerize to a solid. This is called "Low Pressure Polyethylene" but it has a higher melting point and is more rigid than the original polyethylene. Further discoveries have since been made to simplify its production.

460

Minden, Neb. 68959

Safety Glazing, 1972 – Laws were passed in several states during 1972 and 1973 requiring that safety glazing be used in buildings to prevent bodily injury from flying glass in an accident. Warp's Flex-O-Glaze, a clear, rigid acrylic plastic for windows made by Flex-O-Glass, Inc. (Warp Brothers division), was the first plastic safety glazing to be approved by the Safety Glazing Certification Council, on February 25, 1972. It was given Number SGCC118, to comply with laws for safety glazing materials used in buildings.

461

It was first to be approved for safety glazing.

Minden, Neb. 68959

The anopheles mosquito that carries malaria is smaller than most mosquitos and it gets smaller with age. While developing louvered window screening, Harold Warp cut louvers in the bottom of an aluminum pie plate. He was primarily interested in keeping out the malaria mosquito, as they breed only in warm climates, where a shade screen would be most practical. Mr. Warp actually raised anopheles mosquitos to determine the number of louvers he needed per inch of screening. It required 17 louvers per inch to entrap the starved mosquitos. Mr. Warp found by experimenting that the standard 16 mesh window screen does not keep out malaria mosquitos. That is why Warp's shade screen has 17 louvers per inch.

462

Warp raised anopheles mosquitos to test his patented venetian screen against them (the Malaria mosquito).

NEW KIND OF FLY SCREEN

KEEPS ROOMS COOLER

Warp settled his patent rights and infringements on a train with Ingersoll.

Ewing and Grebe in Michigan obtained a patent on a woven insect/shade screen and Harold Warp obtained a patent on an insect and sun screen stamped from a solid sheet of metal, unbeknown to each other in 1940, as the patents issued in different categories. Ewing and Grebe sold their patent to the Borg-Warner Corp., who sued Warp for patent infringement, as Ewing and Grabe's (woven) patent issued a few days prior to Warp's (stamped out) patent. Warp counter-sued, for the patents had issued in different categories. Before the case came to trial, Mr. Warp was traveling to Chicago by train when he noticed the man sitting across from him was Roy Ingersoll, President of Borg-Warner Corp. Harold Warp introduced himself to Roy Ingersoll and told him "We have a case you and I can settle on this train today, if you are willing, and we can call our attorneys off the case." Mr. Warp suggested to Mr. Ingersoll that they cross-license their patents for $1 per year, thus keeping exclusive rights to both types of screening. Mr. Ingersoll agreed; that ended the controversy over patents that day on the train.   463

Sears and Wards offered their first plastics in 1928.

Both Sears, Roebuck and Montgomery Ward reluctantly listed their first "plastic" (storm window) in their 1928 catalogs. In order to make it easy for them, Harold Warp furnished them with the copy, wood cuts and also named the products for them.   464

The trademarks Celloglass and Vimlite worthless to others.

When DuPont offered Harold Warp their "Celloglass" and the Celluloid Company offered Warp their "Vimlite" after trying to compete with his "Screen Glass" and Flex-O-Glass for many years, he told the DuPont officials, "when the DuPont name will no longer be associated with the name Celloglass, it will be worthless." He told officials of the Celluloid Company the same, consequently Celloglass and Vimlite were dropped in the 1960s. (Warp's Screen-Glass was still being sold in hardware stores in 1992.   465

H. Warp's helper almost drowned in Flex-O-Glass mixing vat.

In the preparation of ingredients from which Warp's Flex-O-Glass was manufactured, Harold Warp never patented a secret discovery. He found that cooking the mixture, then cooling it overnight caused it to jell. A vat 12 feet high held the mixture with an elevator that carried the ingredients to a trap door on top of the heated tank. One evening in 1935, Mr. Warp was busy in the office, while his helper was tending the vat. He heard the man screaming for help. Mr. Warp ran out in the factory to find the man up to his armpits in the trap door at the top of the heated vat. He had climbed to the top of the vat to change a light bulb and accidentally fell through the trap door. Luckily, his outstretched arms saved his life. Mr. Warp rushed him to the emergency room in a nearby hospital, concerned about how badly the man's body was scalded. Luckily, as they cut off the man's clothing, the only places he was badly burned was around his waist where his belt had been, and around the tops of his shoes. 466

HAROLD WARP
PIONEER VILLAGE
Minden, Neb. 68959 FOUNDATION

Union Carbide Corp. tried to stop Warp from making "Skin-Pack" packaging that he had originated.

When the first transparent packaging was developed by Harold Warp and his helpers in the early 1950s, three different patent applications were filed in the U.S. Patent Office. Mr. Warp was interested only in manufacturing the plastic. Therefore he applied for a patent on the transparent packaging plastic and method of production. The Rhinelander Co. in Wisconsin applied for a patent on the paper board and perforations. Abott applied for a patent on the machine for making the transparent packaging. The only patent that issued was on the Abott machine. Union Carbide Co. purchased Abott's patent and proceeded to sue Harold Warp for a royalty on his plastic used with the Abott packaging machine. They were unsuccessful however. Warp was able to prove that he was the initiator. After developing the transparent packaging, it was several months before Warp received his first order, which was from the Eversharp Pen Company in Chicago, again proving people resent change. 467

Mr. Russell was seeking a license to produce a product on which Harold Warp had a patent. A meeting in Mr. Warp's office was agreed on at a future date. Mr. Warp had a winter home in Florida from where he came the day of the Chicago meeting. When Russell walked in Warp's office he saw a picture taken of Mr. Warp with fish caught at Ft. Lauderdale, Florida. He said "Do you get to Florida often?" and Mr. Warp replied "Occasionally." "Where to?" he asked and Mr. Warp replied "Royal Plaza Drive in Ft. Lauderdale." Russell replied "I live across the channel from you, on Royal Palm." They had both traveled from Ft. Lauderdale, Florida to Chicago that day for their meeting, when they could both have stayed in Ft. Lauderdale. 468

Mr. Russell and H. Warp could have met as Florida neighbors; instead they traveled to Chicago.

Harold Warp has truly been a pioneer in plastics. Before his new industry was put under the broad title of Plastics, Warp's were turning out Flex-O-Glass. Getting listed in the yellow pages telephone directory in the mid-1920s was a problem. Plastics were unknown, so there was no listing. Harold suggested a heading Glass Substitutes, but this required two or more manufacturers. Consequently Flex-O-Glass was first listed under Glass in the yellow pages. 469

Chicago's yellow pges telephone directory would not list "plastics" or even "glass-substitute" for Harold Warp when he started manufacturing Flex-O-Glass in 1924.

Edwin H. Land, inventor of the Polaroid camera, got the idea for an instant photo when he took a picture of his 3-year-old daughter. She asked why she had to wait to see the picture. He introduced the first instant camera in 1947; its photos required 60 seconds to develop. Among his more than 500 patents, his first was polarized sun glasses, while still in college. He died in February, 1991, age 81. 470

When Ed Land's daughter asked why she had to wait for the picture he took of her, it gave him the idea for an instant camera.

Before Harvey Firestone started making tires for Henry Ford's Model T, his first venture was a patent on a pair of wire grippers to draw the two ends of the wire together for welding, that went through the hard rubber buggy tires. (There was a hole lengthwise in all buggy tires, through which a wire would be strung and welded together where the ends of the wire came together.)   471

Harvey Firestone's first patent was a gripper to hold the wire through buggy tires, while welding it together.

Before we had dentist's offices, barbers pulled teeth. Then after the Civil War, traveling dentists would go from town to town, carrying their dental equipment and supplies in a carrying case. They would usually run an ad in the local newspaper stating what day, or days, they would be in the town. One of these traveling dentist's equipment and carrying case, that belonged to Wm. B. Crosley is on display at the Harold Warp Pioneer Village at Minden, Nebraska, as well as the dental equipment that was used by early day barbers.   472

Dentists traveled from town to town, carrying tooth pulling equipment in a wooden case, before they opened offices.

When Nat Currier set up his lithograph shop at No. 1 Wall Street in 1834 the only way to get to California was by covered wagon or clipper ship. Eighteen years later he hired James Ives and by the time Ives retired in 1895 a network of railroads bridged the country and telegraph messages flashed from coast to coast in a matter of minutes.

During the interim years Americans looked to Currier and Ives to provide lithographed pictures of every major event, famous fights or horse races as well as colored portraits of leading political figures at 5¢ to 25¢ each to hang in barber shops and saloons. These men also made colored lithographs of American scenes to hang on the walls of homes. They worked for the present, never dreaming their lithographs would increase in value a thousand fold in the next century and that they were leaving a living record of history in the making during this transition period prior to invention of the photograph.

CURRIER and IVES

They left a living record in colored lithographs.

Nat Currier, who came from Roxbury, Massachusetts, was twenty-one years old when he made his first timely lithograph for sale, entitled "Ruins of the Planters Hotel, New Orleans, May 15, 1835." This was followed by "Blasting of the Merchants Exchange in the New York Fire of December 16, 1835." "The Dreadful Wreck of the Mexico in Hamstead Beach" and scores of other newsworthy pictures. Artists were employed to make the original drawings and these were transferred to the lithographing stones by Nat himself. J.H. Bufford drew the first two of the above catastrophies. Later Louis Maurer painted Indian scenes, W.K. Hewitt painted ships and eventually many more artists were hired.

The great fire at Chicago, October 8, 1871.

Nat Currier hired James Ives, eleven years younger than himself, in 1852 to keep his books as well as draw and make lithographs. Ives, then twenty-eight, was a forceful, witty, headstrong, young New Yorker, and didn't mind offending people, contrasting to the more cautious, pompous Mr. Currier. Ives made an immediate hit with the other artists and within weeks had completely revamped the entire business of "N. Currier, Lith.", then occupying three floors at 33 Spruce Street in New York.

Ives reorganized the art work on the mass production basis, since adopted by Walt Disney. This meant that nearly everyone worked on every print. Fanny Palmer generally did the backgrounds while Maurer, Worth or Tait would do the figures. Currier and Ives supervised the over-all production, thumbing through rough sketches to decide what would sell best.

When a drawing was finally okayed, it went to the shop's lithographers who were presided over by John Cameron, a man who loved the bottle. If Cameron was off on a toot, Currier and Ives, both expert lithographers, were apt to do his work. Their problem: to transfer the drawing to a flat stone, then print from the stone's impression.

The stones were imported from Bavaria and specially prepared. Two flat stones were rubbed together, with a layer of fine flint dust between them, producing on the stone's surface a very fine "grain" consisting of innumerable tiny depressions. When the drawing had been placed atop the stone in the heavy press, the screw was then turned down tightly. This transferred the drawing to the stone, forcing the greasy crayon into the stone's "grain." Then gum arabic and nitric acid were poured over it. The gum arabic desensitized areas not drawn on while the acid ate away stray grease particles. The drawing itself was protected by the crayon's wax.

Then the greasy image itself was washed off with turpentine, leaving the drawing apparently destroyed. The stone was then dampened with water so that the ink, which contained grease and had a natural affinity for the grease in the "grain," was repelled wherever no drawing existed.

Winter moonlight "Christmas Eve".

The stone was then ready for printing. Almost any number of prints could be reproduced. They then washed off the image and reground the stone for a new drawing. Currier and Ives produced so many prints — some 8,000 subjects — that they employed one man to grind stone surfaces. For that reason no Currier and Ives engraving stones remain in existence today.

Most of the time Currier and Ives got along like a well-matched team. Nat, recognizing Ives' unusual talents, made him a full partner in 1857, after five years. (Nat generally paid low salaries; Louis Maurer, his best artist, finally quit after many years because Nat would not pay him $25 a week.) But once Ives became a full partner, there were many times when their private disagreements threatened to demolish the firm. Finally Ives dumfounded Currier by enlisting, saying to Currier: "I'm through with business until the war's won."

Currier retired in 1880 and Ives followed fifteen years later. Neither lived long after retiring. Their sons, Edmund Currier, son of Currier by his first wife, and Chauncey Ives tried to run the business. But its sales dwindled and finally in 1907 the firm disappeared. (Currier and Ives employed these men, who became outstanding artists of their time: Thomas Nast, Louis Mauer, Eastman Johnson, George Catlin) 473

HAROLD WARP
PIONEER VILLAGE
Minden, Neb. 68959 FOUNDATION

John James Audubon

John James Audubon was born April 26, 1785, while his French Navy officer father was stationed in Haiti. His mother died at an early age. He spent his boyhood on his father's estate in France, where he developed a talent for drawing, love of the outdoors, natural history and the study of birds in particular. When still in his teens he migrated to America and tried to establish himself in the milling business on his father's 300 acre farm on the Perkoimer River near Philadelphia.

He married Lucy Bakewell and while trying for commercial success he traveled to Kentucky in 1808 and New Orleans in 1812. He finally resorted to painting portraits to feed his family. He loved the outdoors, enjoyed painting birds and animals, and succeeded in selling a few wildlife sketches, too.

Woodpeckers

In the autumn of 1820, when he was 34, he set out in pursuit of a dream that would take him years to realize and would require long visits to Europe and back into the woods, swamps and coastlines of America, where the birds of the continent lived in fantastic abundance. It would also mean near poverty for his wife and children and long periods of separation from them. But his wife, Lucy, mentioned none of the hardships when she wrote in a letter to a relative that her husband was in Louisiana "prosecuting a large work on Ornithology which when compleat he means to take to Europe to be published. The birds are all drawn from nature the natural size and embellished with plants, trees or views as best suits the purpose."

Orioles

The result of all this sacrifice was "The Birds Of America," a double-elephant folio of prints priced at the fantastic amount, in those days of the 1830s, of $1,000 per set. 200 sets were issued. Each set contained 435 full-color folio-size paintings of 1065 American birds. It was soon recognized as "one of the most precious documents in the archives of American art." Audubon's paintings were left to his widow, following his death on January 27, 1851. In 1863 they were bought by the New York Historical Society, in whose collection they still are. Audubon spent the last few years of his life at a home he built on the Hudson river. — Gleaned in part from THIS WEEK, 10-2-66 by T.H. Mulligan   474

700,000 Sandhill Cranes stop in Nebraska March to April 10.

Highest Crane concentration 10 miles north of Pioneer Village Hotel.

Beginning in late February every year hundreds of thousands of Sand Hill Cranes congregate along the Platte River from Grand Island to Lexington, Nebraska. The largest concentration of them will gather between Kearney and Gibbon, where the Platte River is at its southernmost point. The Audubon Society has purchased the Platte River bed for several miles east from the I-80 bridge to the Pioneer Village. They forage in nearby fields by day and spend their nights in the Platte River shallows. The greatest numbers will be in March. By April 15th, they have all gone north to the Arctic Circle, where they nest and raise their young. Diggings in this area have uncovered crane bones that were deposited here thousands of years ago.

475

HAROLD WARP
PIONEER VILLAGE
Minden, Neb. 68959   FOUNDATION

Lowell Depot was the end of the railroad in Homestead days. On May 6, 1870 Congress authorized the B & M to build a railroad west from Chicago to Fort Kearny, Nebraska, where it was to connect with the Union Pacific on the north bank of the Platte River. George B. Skinner, a surveyor who preceded the railbed, reported that he would give a dollar for every ear of corn that could be raised west of Fort Kearny.

Then in 1872 the Union Pacific refused to connect up with the Burlington at Kearney unless shippers paid the Union Pacific an extra rail fare from Omaha, 200 miles away. This U.P. ruling was later upheld by Congress.

Homesteaders arrived at this Lowell depot and range cattle left.

As a result, Lowell, Nebraska, eight miles east of Fort Kearny, became the western terminus of the Burlington Railroad during the ten years that western Nebraska and Kansas was surveyed and taken up by homesteaders (1872 to 1882). During these ten years the entire plains country, between the Platte and Republican Rivers, was homesteaded or settled by pioneers, many of whom disembarked at Lowell, or came overland by ox-cart and covered wagon.

As new settlers arrived at this depot in cattle cars and boxcars, with their dairy cows, work horses and few belongings to go forth to fence this virgin country, the range cattle were shipped back East in the same cars. In the 1870s Lowell had a signal light that was hoisted at night and could be seen for many miles by the Texas rangers, who were driving their cattle north by the thousands, to this very depot for shipment east.

As the years went by Lowell Depot became a forgotten sentry in the sand hills of Nebraska. Civilization had passed it by. It had served its purpose well and was no longer needed.

Seven worn-out floors were found in it.

In 1950 the Burlington Railroad decided to dispose of this old depot. Permission was granted Harold Warp to move it to a permanent home at his Pioneer Village, rather than see it destroyed. When the men started to restore it, seven layers of worn-out flooring were found in this old landmark. He had another reason for wanting to preserve it. Onto one of these seven floors his mother, Helga Johannesen Warp stepped off the train from Norway on June 24, 1878, at the age of sixteen — when she and her brother, Johannes, with his wife and family of four children arrived to take up a homestead on the divide twenty-five miles south of Lowell.

Helga Johannesen was truly a pioneer in the highest and finest meaning of that fine word. With her brother, she came from Yntra Arna, near Bergen, Norway, when she was sixteen, and homesteaded in Nebraska, next to another pioneer, John Warp.

Sod house on Nebraska homestead.

John Warp had come from Skollenberg, Norway, and lived in a neighboring dugout. Before you knew it he and Helga Johannesen, in the manner of young folks the world over, were in love. They were married in 1880. To this union, twelve children were born on that pioneer Nebraska homestead, Harold Warp being the youngest.   476

HAROLD WARP
PIONEER VILLAGE
FOUNDATION
Minden, Neb. 68959

People Resent Progress — While most people dislike work, or pretend to dislike it, they fear the consequences of lack of work and naturally resent the encroachment of technology on their livelihood. It has always been so.

**Grain Threshers
One Century Separated Flail
and Combine**

Flail
The First Thresher

Some of the first threshing machines, replacig the flail, were powered by treadmills, which first came into general use in the U.S. in the 1850s.

Horsepower threshing became popular in the 1890s.

The Steam Threshing Rig, 1910.

The Grain Combine
1930

When power from wind, water, steam and electricity in turn replaced human muscle, those whose muscles were replaced revolted and fought the innovations with whatever weapons they had. Their resistance was futile.

Hand sawyers in England wrecked the new water-powered sawmills.

In the Low Countries, when machines began to take the place of textile workers, they responded by throwing their wooden shoes into the machinery. From this we get our word "sabotage".

Iron was originally smelted with wood charcoal, but, by 1600, the forests of England showed signs of depletion. In 1621 Lord Dudley received a patent for making coke from coal and using it in smelting. But the charcoal burners wrecked his furnaces.

Ned Ludd may, or may not, have been a real person, but, in the early 1800s the Luddites, who called him their King, were a very real factor in industrial England. They were opposed to all mechanical innovations and systematically destroyed the new industrial machinery. Their riots were ultimately met with punitive legislation and in 1813 a mass trial of Luddites resulted in many hangings.

Bartelemy Thimmonier, a French tailor, invented and built sewing machines. These were made of wood and had little resemblance to the later machines of Howe and Singer, but by 1841, some eighty of them were in use in Paris. In that year a mob wrecked Thimmonier's shop and nearly killed the inventor.

Mobs also wrecked Hargreaves' spinning jenny. Rivermen on the Weser wrecked Papin's steamboat. Scottish typesetters ruined the stereotype plates of Robert Gar. Sailing vessel captains rammed Fulton's steamboat. Steam engine crews sabotaged Davidson's electric locomotive. Charles Welch had to guard his coal-mining machinery with a gun. Ericsson's steam fire engine was assaulted by the bucket brigades.

All of these inventions ultimately benefited mankind and similar benefits continue increasingly.

477

HAROLD WARP
PIONEER VILLAGE FOUNDATION
Minden, Neb. 68959

Sharps Buffalo Gun
"It decimated the buffalo."

The Sharps Buffalo Gun, introduced in 1869, was a .45 - 120 - 550 caliber, had a bone front sight and double set trigger. Because of its remarkable accuracy, the word "Sharp-Shooter" originated. Although the firm failed in 1874 and only 2,000 of these guns were made, it was considered one of the greatest rifles ever made in America, being responsible for decimating fifty million American bison on the Nebraska and Kansas plains.

Often only the tongue was taken. The wanton slaughter of these beasts caused many Indian attacks, for Indians depended on the American bison for food. By 1905 there remained only 900 "buffaloes" in the entire United States, at which time they were put under protection.   478

The stone in the fireplace in th 1830 kitchen at Warp's Pioneer Village in Minden, Nebraska, came from the old White House in Washington, D.C., when it was rebuilt in 1951.

The two tons of stone in this fireplace came from the White House when rebuilt in 1951.

The White House, originally built in 1792, burned by the British in 1814, was rebuilt in 1818. It then stood 133 years until rebuilt in 1951. Arrangements were made with Congressman Curtis to purchase enough stone to make this fireplace of 1830.

The bluish colored stone is Mica Schist. The lighter colored is Sandstone.   479

The inspiration that sparked the Wright Brothers to build gliders in their spare time, before they invented the flying machine, was a set of plans by Otto Lilienthal, a German engineer who had invented the curved wing surfaces for a glider, but was killed in one of his own gliders in 1896. In their experiments with gliders they found some of Lilienthal's principles incorrect, so they set up their own crude wind tunnel in 1900 and took accurate readings of what happened that are fundamentally the same today.   480

Wilbur Wright testing flight characteristics of wing sections wired to his handlebars, while whizzing down Germantown hill in 1900.

The 9N Ford tractor incorporating the Ferguson System was placed in production in the United States by the Ford Company, Dearborn, Michigan, in 1939. This 2-plow tractor was powered with a 4-cylinder vertical engine and fitted with a 3-point hydraulic lift to which a plow or other equipment could be attached. By a small lever the attached implement could be raised or lowered at will with little effort. The claim was made that the suction of the plow pulled down on the rear wheels thereby increasing their traction.

The Ferguson System was perfected in 1935 after 17 years of engineering development by Harry Ferguson. His invention featured a hydraulic system built into the tractor to operate implements as an integrated unit, and within two years approximately 1260 were manufactured and sold in the British Isles and Norway.

Henry Ford II didn't think much of his grandad Henry's verbal agreement with Harry Ferguson until Harry collected $9,250,000 from Henry II.

Late in 1938, Mr. Ferguson brought his tractor and equipment to the U.S. and demonstrated it to Henry Ford. A verbal agreement was made between Mr. Ford and Mr. Ferguson for mass production of a tractor incorporating the Ferguson System. Under this arrangement more than 300,000 tractors were built between June 1, 1939 and June 30, 1947. After the death of Henry Ford, Sr., Ford commenced making their own 3-point suspension tractors in 1947 and Ferguson came out with their own tractor in 1948. Harry Ferguson subsequently sued Ford for $251,000,000 for breaking the oral agreement he had with the late Henry Ford, Sr. The case was settled April 9, 1952 for $9,250,000 in damages. 481

When he was 39 years of age, Henry Ford told his brother in 1902, "I can make dollars racing, but I can't make ¢ manufacturing." At the time, Ford had failed twice. 482

Millionaire R.E. Olds retired the year Henry started making Fords. Both men were 40. (January, 1904) 483

In 1902 Henry Ford sold his patent on the carburetor for $1800 to the men who named his first car, "Cadillac". Henry had insisted the car not be called Ford because it had only one cylinder. He wanted more power, so he put a two cylinder engine under the seat of an identical chassis. That was the first Ford sold. After that he paid little attention to patents. The first Cadillac and that first two cylinder 1903 Ford stand side by side at the Harold Warp Pioneer Village in Minden, Nebraska.   484

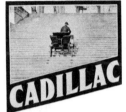

Henry Ford designed the first Cadillac in 1902. In 1912 it had the first electric self-starter.

Charles F. Kettering was born on an Ohio farm. After teaching a country school for three years he graduated from Ohio University in 1904 as an engineer and became a very successful inventor. His first major invention was to power an adding machine with an electric motor. He put the first self starter on a Cadillac in 1912, working in a barn loft. He went on to develop the Delco light plant for farmers, Delco ignition systems on cars, ethyl gasoline and two cycle diesel engines, among his many inventions. He died in 1958, age 82, then worth an estimated $50 million.   485

It was discovered in 1924 that chicks kept under glass died, but the sun's ultra-violet rays that passed through Warp's Flex-O-Glass allowed chicks to grow big and strong.

In 1926 ten square yards of Warp's Flex-O-Glass was sent to various State Experiment Stations, to test as windows in baby chick brooder houses, in comparison with common glass. It had been discovered by Harold Warp that chicks kept behind common glass would actually die for lack of the sun's ultra-violet rays, stopped by glass. But chicks kept behind his Flex-O-Glass, that let the sun's ultra-violet rays pass through, would grow strong and healthy. Naturally Mr. Warp was anxious to have State University Experiment Stations conduct tests to verify his claims.

At the University of Wisconsin's Experiment Station, in addition to testing Warp's Flex-O-Glass in comparison with common glass, Mr. Halpin decided to irradiate corn kernels with actinic rays from an arc lamp (then used as a source of light in

Wisconsin University irradiated milk with ultra-violet rays (vitamin D) from an arc lamp rather than from the sun. They patented it and proceeded to collect millions of dollars from milk processors annually who commenced adding vitamin D to their milk.

In 1930 DuPont chemists obtained animal spinal cords from packing houses and irradiated them. They packaged this and sold it to add to animal and chick feeds as "Vitamin D" (to replace sunshine).

The Trico Feed Mill retained alfalfa's vitamin D (sunshine) in these huge storage tanks by replacing the air in them with burned natural gas.

By 1990 skin lotion manufacturers were advertising the sun's ultra-violet rays (nature's vitamin D) as a cause of skin cancer and recommended their "sun-blocker" skin cream be applied when exposed to the sun.

showing movies). They then fed the irradiated corn kernels to one pen of chicks alongside those behind Flex-O-Glass. It worked. The chicks grew, so they proceeded to shine the light from the arc lamp on butter instead, and that worked too. They then irradiated milk with the arc lamp and found that chicks grew strong and healthy on ultra-violet radiated milk. They then patented the irradiation of milk naming Wisconsin University as patentee, who collected millions of dollars in royalties from milk processors, nationwide, for many years thereafter.

DuPont's chemists became interested and in their experiments they found that the spinal cord of livestock, being processed at packing houses, would absorb large amounts of ultra-violet rays from an arc lamp. DuPont patented this method of retaining actinic rays (vitamin D) and proceeded to offer dried, granulated irradiated spinal cord to animal and chicken feed processors, as a high source of vitamin D. Feed mills nationwide commenced adding DuPont's "Vitamin D" to their feeds in the early 1930s.

It was also discovered that certain plants would absorb high percentages of the sun's ultra-violet rays. Among them an aquatic plant eaten by codfish and also alfalfa. It was soon discovered that alfalfa, when dried and stored for winter feed, would lose most of its vitamin D, unless kept in an oxygen free storage tank.

In 1940 Harold Warp and his associates built an alfalfa dehydrating plant near Minden, Nebraska, including a natural gas burner to remove the oxygen and a still to remove the moisture from the gas. The oxygen-free, dried gas was then fed into large tanks, full of dehydrated alfalfa, as air was removed. Thus the vitamin D was retained in the alfalfa.

Between 1924, when it was discovered that the sun was the source of the health-giving (vitamin D) rays and 1990, when many pills and foods contained vitamin D, originally found in sunshine, folks in 1990 commenced screening the sun's ultra-violet rays out of their sun-bathing with special skin creams, for fear of getting skin cancer. **486**

High on a mountainside in South Dakota's Black Hills are the gigantic faces of Washington, Jefferson, Lincoln and T. Roosevelt, looking out over the grassland, buffalo herds, fossilized Badlands and tourists. But they didn't come to be there as easily as anticipated; fourteen years, to be exact, from August 10, 1927, when they commenced chiseling the top of Washington's head until 4 p.m. on October 31, 1941. That October afternoon the chiseling crew of miners melted away, after many layoffs for lack of funds during those depression years.

It took 350 miners, swinging high on a mountainside, at 50¢ to $1.25 per hour, 14 years to gouge out 900,000 tons of rock, at a cost of $989,993.32, and untold hardship, to sculpt these four faces. The U.S. government then built a road so folks could see them, at a cost of $2,000,000.

On September 24, 1924, John de la Borglum first arrived at Rapid City, at the invitation of South Dakota's Historian Doane Robinson, who had envisioned carvings of Buffalo Bill, Chief Red Cloud and other Old West characters on the "Needles" that are free standing Black Hills granite spires. Borglum, who had just completed a carving of Robert E. Lee on Georgia's Stone Mountain, envisioned a huge figure of George Washington carved on Mt. Rushmore instead. That evening (9-24-24) Borglum told a spellbound South Dakota audience he would carve them a great National Monument on Mount Rushmore and stated, "It won't cost you a dollar." He said it would be paid for by his wealthy friends.

John Gutson Borglum had just completed a bust of Robert E. Lee on Stone Mountain, Georgia in 1920 when he was contacted to do a sculpture of Buffalo Bill and Chief Red Cloud, on the Black Hills' granite spires. Borglum envisioned a huge bust of George Washington on Mount Rushmore instead.

John Gutson de la Mothe Borglum was born March 25, 1876 in Idaho, to Danish immigrants, who soon moved to Fremont, Nebraska, where he grew up. Having talent for art, he studied in California and in Europe during the 90s and in 1902 set up a studio in New York City. His ambition was to carve colossal art on mountains and his ambition came true in 1915, when the Daughters of the Confederation asked Borglum to carve a 20 foot square tablet of Robert E. Lee on Georgia's Stone Mountain. He said "Ladies, a twenty-foot head of Lee on that mountain would look like a postage stamp on a barn door." He contracted to do a sculpture on Stone Mountain, supposedly for a fee of $14,000, but World War I interferred and work did not start until 1920. Early in 1924 he had completed a beautiful bust of Robert E. Lee, when he was contacted by Robinson in September of 1924, to do a sculpture in the Black Hills of South Dakota.

Almost a year later, on August 25, 1925 Borglum was escorted to Mt. Rushmore by Theodore Shoemaker. He found he had room to carve not only Washington, but also Jefferson, Lincoln and Roosevelt on that near vertical wall of granite, 500 feet long and 400 feet high. When President Calvin and Grace Coolidge arrived at the State Game Lodge in the Black Hills June 15, 1927 for their summer vacation, Robinson thought this could help create interest so he wrote Charles Rushmore, a New York attorney, for whom Mt. Rushmore was named. He responded with a check for $5000, payable to "Mt. Harvey Memorial Association", this was the first money received for the project. Three railroads serving the Black Hills, also the Homestake Gold Mine, each contributed $5000. The Dakota Farmer Magazine put in $2500, making a total of $27,500.

Borglum found he had room to carve Jefferson, Lincoln and T. Roosevelt too. The cost: $350,000 plus 25% for his fee, not to exceed $87,500.

A contract was drawn up between the "Mount Harvey Memorial Association" and Borglum, authorizing the sculptor to "create upon Mount Rushmore Mountain a memorial . . . figures in heroic size of Washington, Jefferson, Lincoln and Theodore Roosevelt". The cost to be $350,000, plus Borglum's fee – "equal to 25% of the cost of the work to be done, but not to exceed $87,500". During August 1927, a two mile road was hacked out to the foot of Mt. Rushmore. Samuel Insull, the Chicago utilities magnate, donated an electric plant to power the work on the mountain. On August 10, 1927, President Coolidge dedicated the Rushmore project by receiving a 21 gun salute, but instead of guns they blew 21 stumps out of the roadway being built. The first actual carving, drilling and rough shaping of the top of Washington's head began October 4, 1927. By December 1927, the money ran out and they were $20,000 in debt.

While Grace and Calvin Coolidge were vacationing on August 10, 1927, Pres. Coolidge dedicated the Rushmore project by dynamiting out 21 stumps as a salute. Coolidge also got Congress to match up to $250,000 with private funds.

During his August 10th speech, Coolidge had casually mentioned possible national government support, so U.S. South Dakota Senator Norbeck decided to see if the President meant what he said, which he did. The result was that Congress approved $250,000, with matching funds to come from private sources. The bill was delayed by

Borglum built a 1/12 scale model. He also built a huge boom and protractor on Mt. Rushmore called a "pointing machine", similar to a "pointer" on his 1/12 scale model.

Borglum's son operated the "pointer" at the top of Mt. Rushmore while his dad hung in a sling on the mountainside dabbing red paint where more rock should be removed.

To get traction for drilling holes for dynamiting, the men would drill two holes about three feet apart, wedge steel pins into the holes and attach a chain around their bodies.

debate and recesses, and finally passed a year later, February 25, 1929. Coolidge signed it six days before his presidency expired. (It was rumored that Herbert Hoover would not have signed it.) Upon passage $55,000 was received from the U.S. Government on June 6, 1929 to match the monies already spent. On June 7, Borglum uncovered the Rushmore machinery that had lain idle for a year and a half and called his former miners back to work.

Working in his studio at the foot of Mt. Rushmore, Borglum had made a 1/12 scale model of Jefferson, Washington and Lincoln. He then had built at the top of Mt. Rushmore a huge protractor and boom that he called a "pointing machine" that his son Lincoln Borglum operated. He had a similar "pointing machine" on his 1/12 scale model. From this the full size dimensions would be transferred to the mountain side to do the carving.

For removing the tons of rock by drills and dynamite, former Homestake Gold Miners were ideal except for one thing. Here they had to hang in mid-air strapped in swing seats suspended on a tiny cable. In the gold mine they had worked standing on solid ground. To get traction the men would drill two holes about three feet apart, wedge steel pins into them and attach a loop of chain around their body so they could push their feet against the cliff to get traction for drilling other holes for dynamiting, etc. Even though they would be laid off from time to time for lack of money for the project, the men became proud of what they were doing here and would usually quit any other job they had taken when called back to work on Mt. Rushmore.

The work went smoothly all summer, but in December 1929, when they had Washington's head and nose formed and his eye sockets roughed in, the money ran out again, but this time the situation was worse because the stock market had crashed that October. Borglum defied defeat. He and the commission tried several fund raising ideas. Borglum suggested a booklet about the Mt. Rushmore project, selling advertising in it; Chairman Joe

Although Washington's head was not completed when dedicated July 4, 1930, Borglum thought it would bring in more money with which to continue the work.

Jefferson's face was first started at the left of Washington, but was scuttled after 18 months. Here can be seen how the "pointer" was used, visible at top of Washington's head.

The men looked like ants on that huge mountainside.

Cullinan suggested $100 Mt. Rushmore membership fees and John Boland, business manager proposed 10¢ grade school student donations and high school students a quarter. Borglum's booklet idea brought in $10,000, Cullinan's Mt. Rushmore Society produced $7200 (although they continued to be a dynamic support organization) but Boland's school children's fund brought in only $1700, (as kids preferred to spend their dimes for yo-yos – which were then the craze). Matched by federal funds, this $18,900 carried the work through the summer of 1930 and the completion and dedication of Washington's head, although at the time it was still in the rough, hardly recognizable, but Borglum thought an early dedication might bring in more money.

In fact Washington's July 4th 1930 premature dedication was very impressive. 2500 spectators, as well as the movie makers, Pathe, Paramount, Fox, Kinogram, and Universal Studio cameras recorded the event as Robinson's grandson, Billy Doane pressed a button that slowly raised an American flag draped over Washington's face, showing ant-like figures of workmen in their cable-hung swing seats being raised along with the flag. While cameras clicked, Borglum, speaking from a pineboard platform declared, "Let us place there, carved high, as close to heaven as we can, their faces – that they will endure until the wind and the rain above shall wash them away." But the spectacular ceremony failed to raise any funds during that drought stricken summer of 1930.

Borglum was determined to keep going, so he purchased five $100 Rushmore Society memberships himself and also donated another $1500. Matched by federal funds, this $4000 carried the work through the rest of 1930. In the spring of 1931 the commissioners themselves scraped together enough money to keep the workmen going until fall, but by December 31, 1931, the commission found themselves $16000 in debt, the workmen laid off and Borglum broke. He wired Senator Norbeck: "The financial situation is such that I am obliged – to shut down the work indefinitely and take up other work awaiting me elsewhere."

After many stoppages for lack of funds, Jefferson's face was finally dedicated by Franklin Roosevelt August 30, 1936.

The machinery was covered once again, buildings shuttered up and the workmen drifted away in search of other jobs. In the spring of 1932 Congress passed a bill authorizing a $300 million U.S. unemployment fund of which South Dakota's share was $150,000. Under heavy pressure from Senator Peter Norbeck, the U.S. Government allocated $50,000 of the $150,000 to the Rushmore project. By some political shenanigans, Norbeck managed to get that 50,000 matched by the government; a matching fund previously passed by Congress. In December 1932, the Rushmore Commission received that $100,000 and Rushmore miraculously rose from the dead after another year of idleness. Also miraculously, nearly all of the original crew came back to work, leaving jobs they had taken, to resume the sculpture.

By 1934, the $100,000 had been used up and Senator Norbeck got Congress to give the Rushmore project the remaining $55,000 of South Dakota's share of the unemployment fund waiving the "matching" requirement. He then introduced a bill for another $200,000 for Mt. Rushmore, grudgingly passed by Congress August 29, 1934. Meanwhile Borglum was having trouble with fissures in the rock. His men peeled away 120 feet of fissured stone before they found solid granite to form Roosevelt's face. (When completed Roosevelt's face was only 30 feet from a canyon in back.) Borglum had first attempted to sculpt Jefferson's face to the left of Washington's, but workmen had found flaws in the granite there also.

OOPS! Subscriber's photo from '30s proves Jefferson's face was begun to the left of Washington, then scuttled and moved to the right.

After 18 months of hard work, Jefferson's half finished face was scuttled by Borglum, the area smoothed off, and he had the men start blasting Jefferson to the right of Washington. The hottest driest year in history was in 1936, but the men continued to work through the searing heat on the sun reflecting granite. Franklin Roosevelt dedicated Jefferson's figure on Sunday, August 30, 1936, while campaigning in South Dakota. This time Borglum had the "pointing machine" swing the American flag away from Jefferson's face. President Franklin Roosevelt said, "I had seen the photographs and drawings of this great work – and yet, until 10 minutes ago I had no conception of its magnitude, its permanent beauty and its importance."

Borglum began to think he was being underpaid, commenced having problems with the National Park Service, but if it hadn't been for his dogged determination, the sculpture would probably never have been completed. He dedicated Lincoln's head himself September 17, 1937.

In 1936, Borglum commenced having problems with the commission and with the National Park Service for wanting to police his spending. He also felt he was being underpaid, but he had no intention of quitting. Also, on December 20, 1936 Senator Norbeck died of cancer. If it hadn't been for his dogged determination to see the sculpture completed, it probably would never have been finished. Borglum dedicated Lincoln's head himself on September 17, 1937. At the microphone he gestured for silence, then cried out: "I will now call the roll of those whose sympathy, understanding and aid has made this memorial possible: Calvin Coolidge, Andrew Mellon, Coleman DuPont, Charles Edward Rushmore, Dr. O'Hara, Peter Norbeck. They are with the gods. We will keep their faith. We will carry on." Then from the top of Washington's head an army bugler played "taps".

With his crew of workers laid off again, Borglum was so unhappy with the commission and Park Service that he went to Washington, D.C. in the spring of 1938 and convinced Senator Ken Pittman of Nevada and Congressman Kent Keller of Illinois to convince Congress to pick a new commission and a new contract, and escape from the former Park Service supervision. In the meantime Congressman Case managed to get Congress to appropriate another $300,000 for Borglum's Rushmore work. Borglum went back to Mt. Rushmore, assembled his largest crew ever, and went back to work on July 7, 1938, after being idle for another six months. He concentrated on Roosevelt's head and he also set a crew to work excavating a "Hall of Records" which had been his dream to carve a cave to house records and artifacts, explaining the present, to generations to come and seal it up tight.

In the spring of 1939, President Roosevelt ordered the Rushmore project returned to the National Park Service and in July a Mr. Williamson of the Park Commission visited the hall and found work-

After Borglum was ordered to stop work on his "Hall of Records", Irving Berlin sang "God Bless America" as T. Roosevelt's head was dedicated July 7, 1939.

When told "This is the last Government money spent on Rushmore," Borglum was on his way to Washington to try and get them to change their minds, when he died March 6, 1942, during a prostate operation in Chicago. Before he died Franklin Roosevelt informed him "the shrine of democracy must give way for the arsenal of democracy."

ing conditions "deplorable". The Park Commission subsequently ordered Borglum to resume work on Roosevelt's head and discontinue work on "Hall of Records," which he did, reluctantly and the "Hall of Records" remained unfinished 50 years later, exactly as it was that afternoon in July 1939, when they quit work on it.

(Theodore) Roosevelt's head was dedicated the night of July 7, 1939. First came fireworks, then flares that lit up the carving. As they burned out, 12 powerful search lights focused on Roosevelt's face as Richard Dennis, a tenor flown in from Hollywood, sung Irving Berlin's latest hit "God Bless America". Borglum, deeply moved, said "I would gladly abandon my sense of accomplishment in all I have done – if I could claim authorship of that one song."

1940 was spent making definite refinements, smoothing the drilling holes in the eye pupils, producing wrinkles and forming hollows and highlights to make the figures more lifelike. He also had a representative from the Park Service, approach the government for an additional $300,000 to carve the busts of the presidents, but the Budget Bureau approved only $86,000, which was a grant by Congress. They also stated "this is the last government money spent on Rushmore". World War II was the reason for the congressional reversal as Hitler had invaded Poland in September 1939.

In early 1941 the 73 year old Borglum was on his way to Washington to try to convince Congress to let him continue his Rushmore sculpture when he stopped in Chicago to see a doctor about his prostate. The doctor recommended surgery which was performed February 17. Blood clots developed that kept Borglum in the hospital where Russell Arundel, the commission's secretary visited him with the crushing news that the "Shrine of Democracy" as defined by FDR, must give way for the "Arsenal of Democracy". One week after Borglum heard there would be no more government money for Rushmore, he died the morning of March 6, 1942 of a blood clot.

About $50,000 remained in the commission treasury and on March 17, 1941 Lincoln Borglum signed a contract with the commission to finish his father's work. He and his crew worked on refinements all that summer. In September they finally started tearing down the buildings and clearing up the debris that had accumulated during the 14 years of carving. Finally on October 31, 1941, after the crew had all scattered, with the money and debris all gone. Mt. Rushmore returned to its timeless silence, with a new face: "America's Shrine of Democracy".

On March 17, 1941, with about $50,000 still available, Lincoln Borglum signed a contract to finish his father's work and clean up the debris.

Very few people thought "that crazy man, Borglum" would be able to turn a mountain into a monument. Over half of the 14 years it took to finish the sculpture were spent either trying to get money to finish the job or waiting for money to continue the blasting. Most of the 350 workers earned 50¢ to $1.25 per hour and 90% of the sculpture was created by blasting. The loyal workmen developed a great respect for Gutson Borglum, who would come down on a cable with the wind blowing him around, study the sculpture, then dab red paint where more granite should be removed. 900,000 tons of granite were blasted from the mountain at a total cost of $989,993.32.

When Rushmore was finally finished the U.S. Government then proceeded to spend many millions of dollars to build a concrete highway to Mt. Rushmore, for tourists. – *Portions gleaned from Rex Alan Smith's article in July-August 1991, America's History.* 487

HAROLD WARP
PIONEER VILLAGE
Minden, Neb. 68959 FOUNDATION

193

Christmas Customs
— Christmas Songs —
How They Came to Be

Terence R. Dw

Christmas Customs
– Christmas Songs –
and
How They Came to Be!

Christmas Celebrations Banned
in Colonial Massachusetts

Christmas celebrations were once banned in America by a stern law. In colonial Massachusetts on May 11, 1659, the legislature passed an antiholiday law which said: "Whosoever shall be found observing any such day as Christmas . . . shall pay for every offense five shillings."

Actually, this law began in England after Puritan politicians gained a stronghold in parliament. The anti-Christmas law went into effect in 1644 as a reaction to celebrations which they felt had lost the inner and spiritual meaning of Christmas. But the harsh measure met with such widespread discontent, including pro-Christmas riots, that in 1655 it was revoked.

The originators of this law in Massachusetts were also Puritans. These persons defined the word "Christmas" to mean Christ-Mass, which they associated with Roman Catholicism.

To these Puritans, Christmas was a "popish Catholic frivolity" at its best and the dread work of Satan in their midst, at worst. So in 1659 the anti-Christmas law was passed, four years after England had repealed a similar law.

This law also proved to be extremely unpopular with Protestants and Roman Catholics alike on this side of the Atlantic. Most colonists, regardless of faith, wanted a special day of gift-giving, feasting, and merrymaking. They didn't feel Christmas should be a day of working.

Even though unpopular, the law was enforced by colonial authorities. And all remained relatively quiet for 22 years without Christmas. Finally, however, the law was rescinded in 1681, but not by the colonial leadership. King Charles II, of England, and his Royal Commission forced its repeal. 488

HAROLD WARP
PIONEER VILLAGE
FOUNDATION
Minden, Neb. 68959

The First Christmas Card, 1843

The now-classic greeting "Merry Christmas and Happy New Year" was printed on a card for the first time in 1843. It was sent by a Sir Henry Cole to a fellow Englishman. In fact Sir Henry commissioned J.S. Horsley to design and print 1,000 of these cards for him. The design in the left panel was entitled "Feeding the Hungry" and in the right panel was "Clothing the Naked". The center panel depicted an English family drinking a toast to the New Year – the mother was holding a mug to the lips of a child too small to lift it.

Even though this drawing created much controversy, the Horsley card of 1843 aroused wide public attention and started the Christmas card fad. The next year many Englishmen sent cards. They appeared in America shortly thereafter, being introduced by R.J. Pease of Albany, New York.

Louis Prang, a lithographer in Boston, who published reproductions of oil paintings and album cards, issued his first line of Christmas cards in 1875. Prang, whose ideas were years ahead of his time, is responsible for the best early Christmas art in America. 489

HAROLD WARP
PIONEER VILLAGE
FOUNDATION
Minden, Neb. 68959

**Thomas Nast
in 1863
introduced the
rotund Santa**

A depiction of Santa in 1858 scarcely resembles the rotund, red-suited fellow of modern times.

A newspaper version in 1944.

Buccaneer style, around 1850.

Thomas Nast's image in 1866.

The First Christmas Tree In America

On Christmas Eve in 1851, Rev. Henry Schwan, pastor of a little Zion Church in Cleveland, Ohio, new arrival from Europe, heard a child's delighted whisper, "Mother, look – the Pastor's got a tree from Heaven!" It was Pastor Schwan's first Christmas with his new congregation, having placed a pine tree lighted with candles in the church, as done in Europe. This was the first tree to shine at an American Christmas service.

It brought on a storm of controversy. The children thought the beautifully decorated tree, glowing with candles, was the spirit of Christmas. But it was a fire hazard. The objectors were determined it should be the last Christmas tree erected in an American church. Schwan wrote letters to other American ministers. A former professor from Germany advised Schwan the custom started in Alsace. The first reference to the decorated, yet unlighted tree, was published in Strasbourg in 1646. Within 50 years the tree crossed the Rhine, picked up lights somewhere en route, and about 1700 turned up in numerous German principalities. Finland had its first tree about 1800, Denmark about 1810, Norway in 1828 and England in 1841.

Pastor Schwan also learned that Jenny Lind, the "Swedish Nightingale", had lighted a tree in Charleston the year before. One letter, from August Imgaard of Wooster, Ohio informed Pastor Schwan that he felled a spruce in 1847 and since decorations could not be bought, made paper dolls and ornaments. On Christmas Eve of 1847 the spruce stood in Imgaard's house, all agleam and inconceivably lovely – the first Christmas tree in America.

But as Christmas approached in 1852 Pastor Schwan had not enough church support to light another tree at his Christmas service. So with great regret he abandoned the hope of establishing the custom. Then on December 24th he received from the pastor of one of Cleveland's older churches the present of a new tree. Rev. Schwan realized immediately that the present meant the acceptance of the custom by churchmen far more influential than himself, and his sadness vanished.

Thus, a Christmas tree shone once again in Zion Church in 1852, and soon the custom spread all through the land. 490

HAROLD WARP
PIONEER VILLAGE FOUNDATION
Minden, Neb. 68959

How Santa Got His Name

Thomas Nast gave Santa his white beard and red suit in 1862 – "Santa Claus" who is accepted by most American children today is the one fashioned in the poem "T'was The Night Before Christmas". This poem was written in 1822 by Dr. Clement C. Moore of New York for his children. However, Moore does not deserve all the credit. He drew strongly from "A History of New York" by Diedrich Knickerbocker.

Moore must be credited, however, with graphically describing the jolly old gent in verse form, his elfin rotundity, merriment, red cheeks, fur suit, and dancing reindeer. To quote from his poem:

"He was dressed all in fur,
　from his head to his foot.
And his clothes were all tarnished,
　with ashes and soot."
"His eyes – how they twinkled!
His dimples – how merry!

His cheeks were like roses,
His droll little mouth
　was drawn up like a bow,
And the beard on his chin
　was as white as snow."

491

HAROLD WARP
PIONEER VILLAGE
Minden, Neb. 68959   FOUNDATION

Origin of the Nativity Scene

The Christmas Crib – In Germany the Christmas Crib is called the *Krippe*. In France it is called the *Creche,* meaning cradle. In Italy it is referred to as the *Praesepe,* or manger. In Spain it is the *Nacimiento,* the nativity scene. A famous American crib is the huge Moravian *Putz* at Bethlehem, Pennsylvania, which sometimes has as many as 200 live animals including sheep, camels and leopards.

The idea for the first Christmas Crib came from St. Francis of Assisi about 1200 A.D. At that time books were not plentiful and common people were illiterate, therefore the religious leaders often dramatized their preaching or used tableaux to illustrate the religious concepts. In this manner St. Francis constructed the first nativity scene as a literal representation of the Biblical story. In a cave in the woods near the cloister, he instructed a friend to build a manger and to fill it with hay. He placed live animals in this stable for the final touch of realism. On Christmas Eve people gathered to view this scene and as they entered the area they stopped in amazement and fell to their knees in adoration. For there was the manger scene much as it was at the Birth of the Child. St. Francis stood before this creche singing the Gospel and telling the wondrous story. This unforgettable occasion inspired other communities to do likewise and the fashion of the Nativity groups spread widely.

492

How Santa Got His Red Suit

The first known illustration of the jolly man was done by W.H. Groome in "Poets of America" in 1840. Although many tried, none caught the spirit of Moore's conception until a young cartoonist for Harper's Illustrated Weekly, Thomas Nast, in 1862 started drawing Santa Claus as we know him today. Nast gave Santa his *red suit* with ermine trim – the Santa that children love today. His original touch was giving Santa a North Pole address.

So, you see Santa Claus is American by birth if not by lineage. Today he is the plump, red-suited Christmas hero of children all over the world.

St. Nicholas, clad as a bishop, came to this country with the Dutch in 1613 when they settled Nieu Amsterdam. Writings in 1820 referred to St. Nichlaus as *Sancte Claus.* It was the Dutch children who truly caused the name of St. Nicholas to be changed to Santa Claus. The English who settled in New York City accepted some Dutch customs, including the arrival of St. Nicholas.   493

HAROLD WARP
PIONEER VILLAGE
Minden, Neb. 68959   FOUNDATION

Christmas Lore

Christmas seals were originated in 1903 in Denmark to raise funds for a hospital to treat children suffering from tuberculosis. Four years later, the first such seals in America were sold in Delaware.

Bells were used in religious ceremonies long before the birth of Christ. "I Heard the Bells on Christmas Day" was written by Henry Wadsworth Longfellow after he heard the Yuletide bells ringing out in 1863.

Alabama, in 1836, was the first state to make Christmas Day a legal holiday.

Although many regard him as a myth, Santa Claus can be traced to a real St. Nicholas, who lived from 280-343 A.D. in Lycia, now part of Turkey. This Christian bishop gave away half his wealth in one of the earliest examples of generous gift-giving.

American poet Clement Moore popularized the concept of Santa in 1822 with his classic poem, "T'was the Night Before Christmas". It was Thomas Nast, a cartoonist of the Civil War era who in 1862 put the finishing touches to Santa Claus as we know him today.   494

HAROLD WARP
PIONEER VILLAGE
Minden, Neb. 68959 FOUNDATION

Christmas Firsts

Setting the Date: December 25 was first assigned as the date for the celebration of the Nativity in about the year 320 A.D. Since the New Testament was written as religious instruction rather than history, the exact date of Christ's birth is not known.

The present day was selected as a means of unifying the observances of Christmas, "the mass of Christ".

Triming Trees: Trimmed Christmas trees first appeared in the United States probably during the American Revolution. An early diary, written at Fort Dearborn, Ill., in 1804 relates the practice of trimming the Christmas tree with ornaments of the time.

At the Round Table: Traditionally, the first Christmas feast in England was held at the Round Table of King Arthur. While the specific date is undetermined, references to the famous king in medieval legends have been traced back to as early at 600 A.D.

At the White House: First National Community Christmas Tree in the U.S. was placed on the White House lawn in 1923, while Calvin Coolidge was President. The tree was a spruce from Coolidge's native state, Vermont.

In the following year Coolidge presided at a ceremony under the sponsorship of the American Forestry Association, to urge the use of living Christmas trees.   495

We Say "Merry Christmas" But . . .

In Norway they say "Gladlig Jul."

Long before Christianity, the Yule season was celebrated in Norway as a festival to the sun, whose strength began to grow again and overthrow the powers of darkness. Early worshippers decorated evergreen trees, hung boughs of mistletoe, and burned logs to celebrate the winter solstice. Yul (or Jôl) fell at about the same time as Christmas (Christ's birth) so when England and northern Europe were converted to Christianity, these customs and the name Yule simply swung over to the new festivities. Many a Norwegian farmer hangs out a sheaf for the birds and gives his stock extra feed on Christmas Eve, while in his house a bountiful table is set and a Yule log burns in his fireplace.

In Italy they say "Bono Natale."

The first of all Christmas carols was that sung in the Heavens by the Angels, "Glory to God in the highest." Historically, St. Francis of Assisi was the first to make the carol popular. He and his followers, in the thirteenth century, composed songs about the birth of Christ and sang them at Christmas time. From Italy the custom of caroling spread to France, Germany, and later to England.

In Holland they say "Hartelijke Kerstgroeten."

Santa Claus is an Americanization of Sante Klaas, Dutch dialect for St. Nicholas, the bearded saint of Europe, who on Christmas Eve carried a basket of gifts for good children and a bunch of birch rods for the naughty ones. The Dutch believed the gifts and sweets should be concealed and disguised as much as possible. The wooden shoe was a logical hiding place so the Dutch children set out their shoes hopefully each year. The New Amsterdam Dutch brought the custom to America and in time the stocking replaced the shoe; thus the custom of hanging stockings by the fireplace is said to be of Dutch origin.

In Spain they say "Felices Pascuas."

The poinsettia has become a Christmas symbol through the beauty of its flaming star flower. Joel Poinsett, a long-ago minister to Mexico, introduced it to America and it has taken his name. In Spain, where it is known as the Flor de Noche-buena, there is deep sentiment for this Christmas flower which grows in abundance and is used lavishly for indoor decoration.

In Germany they say "Froehliche Weihnachten."

 Little German children enroute home from the Christmas Eve church service, which is planned especially for them, are surprised and delighted to see the "Tannenbaum" shining in the windows along the way. This delight reaches a climax when they find a "Tannenbaum" at home waiting for them. The Christmas tree originated in Germany and still plays a major part in the Christmas celebration.

In Sweden they say "Glad Jul."

In the homes of early Sweden little old men called Tomtars with long grey beards and pointed caps crept out from dark corners to do the Christmas cleaning while the family slept. For days before Christmas, the house wives cleaned and scrubbed so that the Tomtars should not find too much to do. The Tomtars legend has disappeared from the present generation but the Swedish wives still prepare lavishly for Christmas. The roast goose, cooked rice, smorgasbord, lut-fisk, and lovely home decorations are traditional.

In Denmark they say "Glaedelig Jul."

When we make our fragrant loaves of Christmas bread, we are following the pattern set by some unknown Danish ancestor. Danish wives saved this Christmas bread until spring when it was mixed with the seed for the fields to bring the gift of fertility. This holy bread contained curative power too when fed to ill men or animals.

496

Poinsettia

The Symbol of Christmas

No matter how many different holiday plants appear on the scene, the beautiful poinsettia plant still remains the traditional symbol of Christmas.

Originating in a rather limited region south of Mexico City near present day Taxco and Cuernavaca, this bright red flower blooming on the slopes during the Advent season (December) was found by a community of Franciscan friars from Spain, and they used it to adorn the Nativity celebration. This custom has become traditional and throughout Mexico the poinsettia is known as the Flower of the Holy Night.

In 1825, Joel Poinsett, a Southern plantation owner and botanist, was appointed to fill the first post of United States Ambassador to Mexico. He was fascinated by this flower when he found it blooming during December around Taxco. He had some plants sent to his home in Greenville, S.C. where they did well in his greenhouse. He distributed this exciting discovery to horticultural friends and thus the name Poinsettia. Because it was a temperate climate plant, it could only be grown in greenhouses. It did grow outdoors, however, in lower Florida and in southern California.

In 1902, Albert Ecke, a Hollywood, California truck farmer, who had immigrated from Germany, began raising poinsettias as a potted plant, but it took 18 years before the Ecke family developed a variety that could be grown as an indoor potted plant.

In 1920, Paul Ecke, Albert's son, introduced the first poinsettia that could be grown indoors successfully and by 1930 this flowers was well on its way to becoming a traditional symbol of Christmas.

In recent years hybrids and various colors have been developed that will stay beautiful for weeks if given plenty of water.

497

Mistletoe, Magical Cure-all Symbol of Good-Luck

High in the tops of trees growing along the Wabash and Ohio river bottoms, among the leafless branches in late autumn and winter waits Indiana's most romantic crop – mistletoe.

Actually, mistletoe is a parasite – a plant that lives off the tree it attaches itself to.

The broad leathery leaves and pearly white berries grow in clumps two and three feet in diameter in the uppermost branches of black walnut, elm and shellbark hickory trees. Birds consider the berries a wintertime delicacy, and in the process of digesting them, transport their seeds to their lofty homes. Under favorable conditions, the seed stays attached to the limb long enough to send out haustoria, the equivalent of roots, which imbed themselves firmly in the bark to create a new plant.

A mistletoe hunter usually finds the plant too high for retrieving from the ground and the upper branches too fragile for climbing. In the past, the solution was to shoot an arrow with a long cord attached up and over the base of the mistletoe. If the flight of the arrow was true, the plant could be dislodged by pulling both ends of the cord.

Harvesting with guns is much more common today. A hunter will aim his gun toward the base of the bright green mass. The more expert the marksman, the cleaner the break and the greater amount of the magical plant that will fall to the ground.

Few plants have had a longer or more romantic history. The ancient Greeks considered it an antidote for poison and other cultures believed it was a magical lock opener, a protection from fire, or a cure for infertility. Its reputation for aiding in friendly relationships probably began with the ancient Norse custom which required enemies in combat, upon noticing mistletoe in the tree branches overhead, to drop their weapons and embrace.

The most persistent attributes claimed for the plant were that it was useful as a magical cure-all and that it was a symbol of good luck. While the medicinal value of the plant is questionable, it is true that research conducted in recent years at the University of California, Los Angeles, has focused on mistletoe derivatives as a cancer retardant.   498

HAROLD WARP
PIONEER VILLAGE FOUNDATION
Minden, Neb. 68959

Origins of Christmas Traditions

Christmas traditions are based on centuries of folklore and legend around the world.

The Christmas tree originally symbolized the Garden of Eden to Germans. The "tree of paradise" was a central theme of their medieval mystery plays, and when these plays were suppressed, the tree (usually a fir) was brought into the home and gradually it became the custom to decorate it with cookies and fruit at Christmas time.

Candles, it is said, were first put on Christmas trees by Martin Luther trying to capture the effect of snow-tipped evergreens sparkling in the moonlight.

Mistletoe is another symbol of Christmas from the annals of legend. The ancient Druids thought it was sacred. Forests in which this precious plant grew were dedicated to their gods. It's said the Druids cut the sprigs with a golden knife and hung them over their doors to pacify the woodland spirits. To the Romans, mistletoe was a symbol of peace and when enemies met under the "supernatural" sprigs they discarded arms and declared a truce. So mistletoe became a symbol of love, and the custom of kissing under the mistletoe evolved.

Christmas stockings, it is suggested, were first hung by the chimney to dry, and St. Nick dropped in a bag of gold by accident. Dutch children set their wooden shoes by the chimney so goodies could be dropped in, but they switched to stockings which would stretch and hold more.

Christmas presents, according to some authorities, took the place of the pagan custom of exchanging gifts at the New Year.

Holly and Christmas are inseparable, but historians say Holly was used in pagan rites long before the Christmas era. In legend Christ's crown of thorns was made of Holly leaves. Male and female flowers are borne on separate trees, but the red berries are only on the female tree.

Christmas Reindeer – Clement Moore's poem in 1822 "T'was the Night Before Christmas" made the reindeer a part of our Christmas tradition. 499

HAROLD WARP
PIONEER VILLAGE
Minden, Neb. 68959 FOUNDATION

The Star of Bethlehem

Why did the shepherds who were tending their flocks, night after night, not see the Star? Could a star really stand still over one place as is claimed in the Gospel? Was the Christmas Star a miracle?

If we knew the exact date of the birth of Christ, there would be no conjecture on the part of science and astronomy with respect to the Star of Bethlehem. It would be a simple matter to find what took place, knowing that science can reproduce for us, in our planetariums, the sky over Palestine two thousand years ago. But there would be this difference: we would interpret the Star position in the sky in the light of modern science, whereas the Wise Men interpreted it according to the theories of their time. Not knowing that the earth was round and revolving about the sun in company with the other planets, they believed the sky to be a "roof" in which the stars were fixed. They constructed the Zodiac and saw in it signs that fitted their philosophies. These Wise Men, knowing that the birth of a King had been prophesied, and ever watching for signs in their great book of the heavens, would be concerned with any incident that might occur among the stars.

Now if we were to sit in a modern planetarium and view the sky over Bethlehem on a night late in February, 6 B.C. (which is the date that astronomers and archaeologists have established for the birth of Christ) we would see in this sky sacred to the Jews, the unusual spectacle of the three planets: Jupiter, Saturn, and Venus in bright conjunction, with Venus, the new-comer, the most brilliant. These Wise Men saw this phenomenon, and linked it with the words of the prophets; the shepherds watchful as they were, might have seen the Star shining brightly but being untutored, viewed it without significance.

Then there is another approach to the theory that the Christmas Star was a fact. The historian-astronomer may assume that the "sign" for Christ's birth occurred four or five years before Jesus was born. So again reconstructing the sky over Palestine in the year 11 B.C., we see a spectacle that was as ominous as it was magnificent. For this phenomenal display was the great Halley comet. Never seen before in the lifetime of those star gazers and Wise Men, it must have aroused much speculation. In their interpretations, a comet meant the death of a Prince, which in turn, would cause speculation upon the birth of a King which had been heralded among them by the prophets for so long.

But, it is the Spirit of the Star that we all love, from whatever angle we look at it – the scientific, the mysterious or the miraculous. The Star continues to spread its light over the earth as it has for two thousand years. It is a beautiful, wonderful symbol of Christmas.   500

HAROLD WARP
PIONEER VILLAGE FOUNDATION
Minden, Neb. 68959

Great Songs of Christmas
and How They Came to Us

"O Come, All Ye Faithful" (Adeste Fideles):

This is one of the oldest hymns in the Christmas service, the first manuscript known to scholars dating from 1751, although the melody is in fact much older. The translation of the Latin words now used in English-speaking countries was made in 1852.   501

"Joy To The World"

Isaac Watts, the son of a Southampton deacon, complained to his father about the boring church music. Using the 98th Psalm as his inspiration "Make a joyful noise unto the world" the teenager produced the song in 1692. Lowell Mason arranged the music for this carol in 1830, using a theme from the "Antioch" portion of Handel's Messiah.   502

The First Noel

Noel comes from the Latin "Natalis" meaning birth. It was first published in England in 1833, but was being sung in France during the sixteenth century.   503

Away In A Manger

Away In a Manger, a well known Christmas carol, was first published in 1887 in a volume entitled *Dainty Songs For Little Lads and Lasses.* The song appeared under the heading "Luther's Cradle Hymn". James Murray who published the volume signed the song with his initials but added the note, "the song was composed by Martin Luther for his children and still sung by German mothers to their little ones."

Since the song is virtually unknown in Germany or anywhere else outside of the U.S.A., it has aroused curiosity. Richard S. Hill traced the first appearance of the words to a poem published in a *Little Children's Book* in 1885 where it appeared unsigned. Mr. Hill also uncovered some forty different musical settings for this poem.

The tune most commonly used today appears on the music. This music gives Martin Luther credit for the music and "M.L." credit for the words. We think this sheet of music should more accurately say, "words - anonymous; music - possibly by James Murray." Whoever the author, this simple hymn is dearly loved and joyously sung by most American children.   504

HAROLD WARP
PIONEER VILLAGE FOUNDATION
Minden, Neb. 68959

Hark! The Herald Angels Sing

The words to this carol came before the music. They were written in 1793 by Charles Wesley, brother of the founder of the Methodist church. One hundred and one years later, the melody appeared in a cantata by Felix Mendelssohn. Then, fifteen years after that, the words and music were joined by Dr. W.H. Cummings, then organist of Waltham Abbey in England. It was presented for the first time on Christ Day 1885.   505

Jingle Bells

J. Pierpont wrote this song in 1857 for a Boston Sunday School choir. This song about the "One Horse Open Sleigh", although a very popular seasonal song, never mentions Christmas.   506

Oh, Little Town of Bethlehem

During the holiday season in 1865, Phillip Brooks, the 30 year old rector of Philadelphia's Holy Trinity Church took a tour of the Holy Land. Christmas Eve he took a peaceful ride from Jerusalem to Bethlehem, past the shepherds in the hills. Three years later he wrote a poem about it and asked organist Lewis Redner to come up with a tune for it. Redner worked on it for a week or more and awoke in the middle of one night in 1868 with the melody running through his head. He got up and wrote the musical notes that night.   507

White Christmas

It was written by Irving Berlin for a motion picture in 1942. Bing Crosby sang it in the film "Holiday Inn" which won the Oscar for best song that year and it went on to be the most popular Christmas song, selling more than 100 million copies.   508

Rudolph the Red-Nosed Reindeer

In 1939, Robert L. May created Rudolph. In 1947, he copyrighted the reindeer with the bright red nose and wrote a book about him for Montgomery Ward, that sold over 100,000 copies. It was based on Clement Moore's 1822 poem titled "A Visit from St. Nicholas." That same year (1947) May's brother-in-law, John Marks wrote the song. It was turned down by Bing Crosby, Frank Sinatra, Dinah Shore and Perry Como. Gene Autry liked the song but didn't think it fit his rugged image. His wife urged him to record it. It was released by Columbia in September 1949, and sold two million copies before that Christmas. Autry's sales since then have reached the 12 million mark, and the total sales by other artists has reached 130 million copies. Mark's royalties have totaled over $600,000.   509

HAROLD WARP
PIONEER VILLAGE
Minden, Neb. 68959 FOUNDATION

The Birth of "Silent Night"

The birthplace of "Silent Night, Holy Night" was high up in the Austrian Alps in the little village of Oberndorf, Austria. Here on Christmas eve in 1818 a young Austrian priest, Joseph Mohr, sat in his church study. Outside the hushed stillness of the night heightened the snowclad beauty of the mountain scene. Inside, his heart was filled with a vision of the peace and joy of the first Christmas tidings, "For unto you is born this day . . . a Saviour, which is Christ the Lord." The thoughts formed themselves into the poem which we now sing. Of course, he wrote them down in German:

> "Stille Nacht, Heilige Nacht!
> Alles schlaft, einsam wacht
> Nur das traute, heilige Paar,
> Holder Knabe im lockigen Haar,
> Schlaf in himmlischer Ruh!"

The next morning, Christmas day, Mohr showed the manuscript to his friend, Franz Gruber, the village schoolmaster and church organist. Gruber was intensely interested and was immediately enthusiastic about writing a perfect melody for those beautiful words.

But mice had nibbled the bellows of the organ! It would be impossible to repair it before the evening service. So Gruber set about composing the accompaniment on the only other musical instrument available, a guitar. Naturally, the accompaniment was simplicity itself. Had the organ been available, he, no doubt, would have embellished the melody with all the ornaments that were in vogue at that time. But the very simplicity lent charm, dignity, and serenity to the verses written by the young priest.

That same evening when the villagers gathered, Mohr and Gruber sang the hymn. Its first audience was deeply touched, and their eyes were filled with tears of joy.

When the man who repaired the organ had finished, he asked Gruber to play something. He played the melody of "Silent Night, Holy Night." The organ-builder liked it and when he returned to his home, he carried a copy of the hymn with him. From his hands it was passed on from one to another.

Twenty-five years passed before the song was printed. Then it spread rapidly throughout the German nation. It was soon translated into other languages and has become the world's best-loved Christmas carol. Its charm has been unspoiled by the years; its message "Christ, the Saviour is born" still brings calm and peace to our hearts. 510

500 Fascinating Facts

INDEX

500 Fascinating Facts

500 Fascinating Facts

500 Fascinating Facts

500 Fascinating Facts

500 Fascinating Facts

219

500 Fascinating Facts

500 Fascinating Facts

500 Fascinating Facts

500 Fascinating Facts